I HUNGRY

The secrets to making food healthy and fun for parents and children

BY RUTH J. KATZ

PUBLISHERS OF O.G AUTHOR GENIUSES

Published by E&R Publishers
New York, NY USA

An imprint of MillsoCo Publishing, USA
www.EandR.pub

Your guarantee of quality

As publishers, we strive to produce every book to the highest commercial standards. The printing and binding have been planned to ensure a sturdy, attractive publication that should give years of enjoyment. If your copy fails to meet our high standards, please inform us and we will gladly replace it.

admin@millsi.co

9781945674563 (Hardcover)
9781945674570 (Softcover)
9781945674587 (Ebook)

Library of Congress Control Number: 2022947288 (application in process)

First Edition

Back cover photos by Luciana Pampalone Photography

DISCLAIMER: THIS BOOK DOES NOT PROVIDE MEDICAL ADVICE
The information, including but not limited to text, graphics, images, and other material in this book in any format, ebook, print, or audio, is for informational purposes only. No material in this book is intended to be a substitute for professional medical advice, diagnosis, or treatment. Always seek the advice of your physician or other qualified health care provider with any questions you may have regarding a medical condition or treatment, and before undertaking a new health care regimen, and never disregard professional medical advice or delay in seeking it because of something you have read on this website.

Dedication

I dedicate this book to my two sons, Jordan and Jonah,
who have grown into strong and healthy adults as a result
of their healthy relationship with food during their childhood.

Thank you to Joshua Rosenthal, the founder of
The Institute for Integrative Nutrition,
whose wonderful program inspired me to write this book.

Acknowledgments

There are so many wonderful people to thank on my road to wellness...
- To my parents Carole and Harvey for their support.
- To Zulu, my deceased African basenji, who opened my eyes to a new way of looking at wellness by needing me to help him with his health.
- To Brad Boles, for helping me write this book and his creativity.
- To my two sons Jordan and Jonah and their healthy appetites and growing bodies
- To my family and friends for putting up with all my countless lectures and pointers on health, and having to order with me and my requests in the restaurants.
- To Geri Brewster RD, MPH, CDN Registered Dietitian, Certified Nutritionist—Thank you for teaching me so much about nutrition. You are so knowledgeable and I highly respect you. Geri's website (www.geribrewster.com).
- To Elexe Abi-Khattar MS, Integrative Nutritionist / Health Coach (www.nutritionin2ition.com/), who edited this book. She has her own practice of educating companies and individuals on nutrition and health. Elexe's website (www.nutritionin2ition.com).

Table of Contents

PART III: Recipes, Resources, Useful Tips

Foreword

Introducing *I Hungry* by Ruth Katz—a book that emphasizes the importance of holistic nutrition for children. This book is perfect for parents, caregivers, and anyone looking to make healthy and delicious meals for kids.

Ruth Katz is a graduate of the Institute for Integrative Nutrition, where she studied the art and science of nutrition and wellness. Throughout her studies, Ruth was drawn to the concept of holistic nutrition, which emphasizes the interconnectedness of the mind, body, and spirit. She realized that this approach was especially important when it comes to children's health and nutrition. As a result, she decided to write a book that would help parents make nutritious and fun meals for their kids.

In *I Hungry*, Ruth provides a wealth of information about nutrition and how it can impact children's health. She discusses the importance of whole foods, organic ingredients, and avoiding processed foods. She also emphasizes the importance of eating a variety of foods, including fruits, vegetables, whole grains, and lean proteins.

What sets this book apart is Ruth's focus on making healthy food fun for kids. She understands that children can be picky eaters and that it can be a challenge to get them to eat nutritious meals. Therefore, she provides creative and exciting recipes that are both healthy and enjoyable for kids. From breakfasts like Rice Cake Face with Nut Butter to snacks like Homemade Fruit Roll-ups to dinners like Zucchini Lasagna, Ruth offers a wide range of delicious and nutritious meals that kids will love.

Additionally, Ruth includes tips and tricks for involving children in the food preparation process. She believes that when kids are involved in shopping for ingredients and preparing meals, they are more likely to enjoy food and learn about healthy eating. Therefore, she provides guidance on age-appropriate tasks for kids in the kitchen, as well as tips for making cooking a fun and educational experience.

Overall, *I Hungry* is an excellent resource for anyone looking to create balance and harmony in their lives and in their children's lives through food. With its focus on holistic nutrition, creative recipes, and tips for involving kids in the meal-making process, this book is a must-have for parents and caregivers who want to ensure that their kids develop healthy, sustainable eating habits.

— Joshua Rosenthal, Founder
Institute for Integrative Nutrition

Introduction

This book summarizes my lifelong journey of struggles, revelations, and wins in restoring balance and harmony in my health. I am proud of my health and how I look and feel. I am sure you want the same. Taking care of my family and myself involves effort and planning, which I lay out in this book. Evolving to be my healthiest self has led me to inspire and educate others along their journeys to wellness.

Parents always ask me, "Ruth, how do you do it? Make it easy for me. Just tell me what to do. Tell me what to buy and what to avoid". They are looking for answers they can't always get from their health professionals, which is where inner wisdom, intuition, and research come into play.

So what is this book about? "I Hungry" will help you to:

- Figure out what foods to feed your family and yourself.
- Make healthier food choices
- Find healthier substitute foods
- Inspire you to try new foods and flavors and step outside your comfort zone
- Feel more confident in the kitchen
- Inspire your kids to want to eat healthier
- Understand why kids are picky
- Learn how to make being healthy more convenient
- Use tips from other parents
- Try recipes of foods to prepare
- Healthy suggestions for food shopping lists
- Most of all, learn what has worked for myself and my family and to be able to integrate this into what works for you and yours.

With love and gratitude,
Ruth J. Katz

A little background info:

I grew up on Long Island, New York. My parents never cooked, nor did their parents. Our freezer was filled with frozen TV dinners and the refrigerator was filled only with baking soda and diet soda. On Monday nights, it was fried chicken cooked in proinflammatory seed oils that have been marketed as a "heart healthy" alternative to butter and traditional saturated animal fats that have been part of the human diet for centuries. Dinners the rest of the week consisted of Chinese food takeout filled with monosodium glutamate (a debatably harmful food additive), pizza made with refined white flour, which increases blood sugar levels and can cause inflammation, and highly processed frozen dinners that contain excessive amounts of additives and preservatives.

Food never seemed important to me. In fact, it was more of an inconvenience growing up having to decide what to eat and how to get it, while leading a busy social life. By the age of 22, I had my own apartment in New York City and was in the real estate business. I danced my way through the early 1990s with fond memories, not to mention high stress levels and pressure to deliver on the job, which further aggravated my irritable bowel syndrome. It wasn't until I was in my 30s that I noticed my unhealthy lifestyle starting to manifest in the form of skin irritations, dry scaly hands and feet, and a chronic abdominal bloat. After months of various doctor appointments and testing, I learned that I was intolerant to gluten and lactose.

These revelations led me to take control of my health and food choices. I simultaneously discovered "Eat Right For Your Blood Type" by Dr. Peter J. D'Adamo, MD, a naturopathic physician. Our blood type may explain why we digest some types of foods better than others due to your biochemical individuality. This book opened my eyes and sent me on a trajectory that changed my life, the life of those around me, and the way I looked at food.

Once I was pregnant with my first son, I was determined to be his road map to a healthy lifestyle and God willing nobody was going to get in my way! I wasn't going to allow my children to mirror my childhood eating habits, so I scoured the bookstores to find all the books I could on children and nutrition. I also enrolled in a nutrition program at Institute for Integrative Nutrition for my health coach certification, and learned about nutrition and staying healthy in a stressful world of overconsumption.

On my wellness journey, I met Dr. Fred Pescatore, MD, a traditionally trained physician having a private practice specializing in integrative medicine, author of New York Times' Best Seller: The Hamptons Diet, and former

Medical Director of the Atkins Center for five years. He opened my eyes to the ALCAT Test, which identifies your food and drug sensitivities.

Avoiding the foods to which you are sensitive allows your gut microbiome to heal, which can improve your mood and energy level and can help optimize your weight. If I can transform my former unhealthy habits into my current healthy lifestyle, so can you!

The one thing that surprises me during the meals I attend with other families and their kids is not only the large portion of food parents allow their kids to consume in a single meal, but also the food choices. At family gatherings and buffets, I let my kids make their own choices because I have exposed them to a variety of tastes and healthy food, so I am confident in their palette and conscious cravings. I notice that they gravitate to whole food options, while other kids go right for sweets and fried chicken nuggets. Since they don't

My mother and me during pre-school

have dessert on a regular basis, they will fill their plates mostly with fruit for dessert.

I must admit that it wasn't always this easy. Because I am a mother with two boys that have tons of boy energy, I've had my tough-mommy moments with lots of "no, you can't have that," "eat your greens," and "sit down and finish your meal." This is an inevitable part of parenting. Often times, I felt I was fighting a losing battle; however, I realized that over time, I was winning! Eventually, when out at a restaurant, my boys started making healthy meal choices on their own. My kids appreciate the foundation with which I have provided them. They have grown into healthy eaters with well-developed muscle and mental clarity. The environment plays a huge role in shaping how your children grow and develop. In the "Nature vs. Nurture" debate, it is essential to nurture your kids for optimal growth and health later in life. Many parents think their kids are eating healthy, but how can they be properly nourished if they are tempted with highly processed foods at school, camps, playdates, parks, and anywhere they go? To be fair, a lot of what the food industry markets as "healthy" is a result of power and influence by big food lobbyists for corn, soy and wheat, pushing their highly processed packaged foods to kids.

According to "The State of Childhood Obesity," the national rate of obesity among kids aged 2 to 19 increased to 22.4% in 2020 up from 19.3% in 2019. We know that obesity is the result of lifestyle choices including poor diet, and lack of exercise.

Luckily, you have the power to vote with your dollar by allocating your money to healthy food options for your kids and your family. I also suggest you start keeping a food journal of what you and your family are eating for at least two weeks. This will help you identify where you fall short in some nutrients and where there may be an abundance (specifically starches, processed foods that contain added sugars and harmful polyunsaturated fats like soybean oil).

I believe we've been sent down the path of American consumerism, where the unhealthiest foods are placed at eye level in supermarkets. This is no accident.

My sons Jonah and Jordan

Supermarkets want you to fill those carts to the brim with addictive hyper-palatable and hypercaloric foods that lack nutrients. Clever marketing techniques complete with colorful packaging are aimed at our children to indoctrinate their minds to always crave sugar-dense and nutrient-poor cereals and snacks. We can prevent our kids from falling victim to corporate advertising by nourishing them with high-quality foods. It is never too late to introduce healthy habits!

PART I

The Road to Wellness

"When Diet Is Wrong, Medicine Is Of No Use;
When Diet Is Correct, Medicine Is Of No Need."

Ayurvedic Proverb

1

Growing Pains and Frozen Dinners

I remember as a child never feeling right. I was thin with a bloated stomach and lacked strength. Looking back, I am certain that I was malnourished. As a result of underdevelopment, my sports performance was subpar and I was always the one picked last for their team. If I had known what I know now about nutrition, sports may have been my hobby.

By the time I reached my teenage years, disco music was all the rage and both my mother and father loved to go out dancing. They are only 22 and 24 years older than me and were very hip. Since she wanted to look good, my mother was always dieting and didn't want to cheat. Therefore, there were never any snacks in the refrigerator, just a case of diet soda called Tab and a box of baking soda. Did she think the baking soda would keep the Tab fresh?

The wonderment of our child and teenage years is that we're not supposed to think about how to run a house or create a shopping list for balanced nutrition, let alone figure out what to eat and portion control. Growing up in my house, "portion control" wasn't even in our vocabulary. Eating everything on our plate wasn't an option, but a rule. I guess my mother thought that frozen dinners counted as portion control as well as a balanced meal, including the apple crumble for dessert. The only benefit I gained was a lifelong fascination with neatly contained compartments like Japanese Bento boxes (which my kids now love) and avoiding toxic containers that house food.

Our pantry was pitiful by today's standards. We had stovetop popcorn that was allowed on my mom's diet and always came out burnt. My father thought he was clever enough to hide his fudge cookies, but I would find them and devour as many as possible. I wondered why I was always starving, and now I know it is because of the lack of nutrients in my diet. My father's idea of breakfast was giving us white flour matzah (an unleavened bread) with chemical-laden margarine on it. This quick breakfast never came with juice or water to wash it down. Due to the lack of satiety from this meal, I knew I had to upgrade this matzah breakfast for my kids when they were growing up in order to provide more nutrients, so they were served a brown rice cake with a smear of almond butter and two banana slices for eyes, a blueberry button nose and a smile made out of orange flavored omega fish oil.

Lunch in the school cafeteria was our only real meal of the day if you could even call what they served "food." It was always washed down with a can of soda. Choices were hamburgers or grilled cheese sandwiches, french fries or instant mashed potatoes, a vegetable like carrots or green beans in a sweet buttery sauce, cookies and an apple. My mother had no idea about even basic food groups when I was growing up and most of the time we were left to fend for ourselves. Back in the day, we didn't have food guidelines. We didn't think to read food labels and we weren't as aware of what we were putting in our bodies as we are today. We were not educated on organic or grass-

Me when I was in 8th grade

fed animals. Our food was and still is pumped full of growth hormones and antibiotics and animal feed made from genetically modified corn and soy that is sprayed with pesticides. These potent chemicals can disrupt your gut microbiome and act as endocrine disruptors, leading to chronic metabolic diseases and is potentially linked to cancer.

Pesticide use is sold on the merit that it prevents damage to the crops and increases crop yield while keeping costs down. However, according to recent research, 94% of farms would lose no production if they cut pesticides and 78% of farms would be equally or more profitable when using less pesticides. Luckily, more people are waking up to the fact that pesticide use can harm both the health of humans and the environment, which is why I advocate organic, regenerative and farm-to-table food!

Unfortunately, the prevalence of both pesticide use and monocrop culture in the USA has depleted the soil of its minerals and diverse microbiome, compromising the nutrient density of the food and leaving us unsatisfied, and most importantly, under-nourished. The complex metabolic processes that occur in the human body require vitamins and minerals as cofactors to carry out enzymatic reactions, so eating food grown in soil with depleted minerals can cause imbalances in our metabolism. Learning about the impact of pesticides brought on a revelation of my childhood: perhaps my chronic hunger and lack of satiety after eating a meal was actually a gut instinct that my body needed more vitamins and minerals because the food being grown in modern conventional soil is not as nutrient dense as food grown under organic conditions in regenerative soil. After researching and learning about where my food comes from, I took an interest in organic, locally and seasonally grown food, as well as farm-to-table. Not having proper nutrients during your growing years can lead to a lifetime of chronic health issues and deficiencies—take me as an example!

My mother couldn't cook to save her life and I remember being upstairs on my bed reading fashion magazines when I heard a loud explosion, followed by the worst smell. I ran down the stairs to discover my mother's failed attempt at boiling eggs exploded and hit the ceiling while she was on the phone catching up on the local gossip with her sister. By the way, she wound up doing this a second time! We still tease my mother about her culinary skills to this day. The point is, the more confident you become in the kitchen, the more your children will reap the benefits in their health and development. As far as actually sitting down at a table for family meals...that never happened in my family. The average family eats dinner together four times a week; however, we were anything but average. Important table etiquette practices such a as holding the fork and knife properly were foreign concepts to us at the time. (More on this in Chapter 7).

Having a tradition of family dinner time encourages your kids to develop healthy eating habits. My brother and I were left to fend for ourselves with a tasteless frozen dinner or take out food loaded with additives, MSG, and industrialized pro-oxidative seed oils full of trans fat. Yes the options were limited, but on a positive note, there was never enough food around the house to worry too much about overeating and gaining weight.

Throughout my busy teens and 20's, I was unknowingly consuming the foods that were damaging my gut and causing anxiety, fatigue, itchy skin and chronic breakouts but I wouldn't find out until years later that I was lactose and gluten intolerant. While my diet was far from perfect, I had begun to establish a solid routine of exercising, starting with dancing. During the

1980s disco era, my parents would host dance classes at our house with all their friends, so I learned to do the Hustle style of dancing.

Being an ambitious and independent teenager, I couldn't wait to get out of the house and be in control of my life. Living in a suburb near New York City, I was also able to get in roller skating and shopping in Manhattan as exercise, not to mention dancing with my DJ boyfriends.

Knowing now the importance of nutrition, it amazes me how my unhealthy diet was able to fuel me through those years, having the energy to jam at local hip bars and work in a clothing store for extra money.

Me in high school

"Most People Work Hard And Spend Their Health Trying To Achieve Wealth. Then They Retire And Spend Their Wealth Trying To Get Back Their Health."

Unknown

2

Finding My Way in an Unhealthy World of Excess

―――――

When I went off to college at the University of Arizona, I was not surprised that I had gained the inevitable freshman fifteen since I had never watched what I ate. The lack of proper nutrition and the fact that I didn't know I had food sensitivities didn't help my study habits. Growing up with my family, I had it ingrained into my head that diet soda was the only option of drinks so I practically lived on aspartame during my college years. Between that and all the unhealthy cafeteria food, I was not of sound body and mind. Luckily, I wasn't raised on fast food and I never touched dessert, thanks to my mother. If I had known what I know now about diet soda, I probably would have opted for water or tea, as the artificial sweetener in diet soda can alter the gut microbiome and actually contribute to bloating, digestive issues, and even weight gain! Since the gut is like the second brain, of course this inhibited my ability to focus!

I chose the University of Arizona for the warm weather and sunshine, which kept my spirits up, but I am New York girl at heart so I transferred my junior year to New York Institute of Technology while simultaneously working for my father in real estate in Manhattan.

I had really found my calling and graduated with a BA in Business and Finance. When I was 22 years old, I could be found at the newest restaurants and clubs, drinking cocktails and socializing. I was on a mission to be an independently wealthy and financially secure businesswoman. I started working in real estate as an appraiser for salary and a real estate salesperson for commission. Despite my successful business decisions, eating healthy still eluded me as I was not aware that my food choices were disrupting my health.

My undiagnosed food sensitivities affected me even more when my career started to take off. Because of my work ambition and long hours on the job, stress entered my life with the pressure I put on myself to succeed. Perhaps my elevated cortisol and constant "fight or flight" mode worsened my abdominal bloat and gas cramps to my breaking point. It was time I started to look at my diet and take control of my health!

I had visited countless doctors and dermatologists and I was simply given topical hand and foot creams for my skin irritations but nothing worked. Instinctively, I knew that the doctors were simply treating symptoms and I would have to take matters into my own hands to get answers, so I listened to my body. The skin is one of the largest organs and a reflection of your health. When there is imbalance, skin irritations are your body's way of communicating to you that you must change something. After all, topical creams cannot correct gut imbalances!

I found a wonderful doctor named Dr. Leo Galland, MD, who is a board-certified internist and has received international recognition for developing innovative nutritional therapies to treat autoimmune, inflammatory, allergic, infectious, and gastrointestinal disorders. He discovered that I was lactose intolerant through a simple breath test, which is not uncommon, as about 68% of the world's population is lactose intolerant. I finally had the answer to what had been ailing me all those years, so I started using dairy alternatives such as milk and yogurt made from almonds or coconuts. Keep in mind that a product with a "dairy free" label does not mean it is healthy—we must also be selective in choosing dairy alternatives due to the additives in these products (oils, sugars, gut irritants). I do not recommend soy as an alternative as most is genetically modified (GMO) and may affect hormones and thyroid health. When I eliminated dairy, I lost 10 pounds of bloat and went down one dress size. I felt so much better without dairy products and my skin rashes and peeling hands and feet disappeared.

It is important to note the difference between lactose intolerance and a dairy allergy. Lactose intolerance refers to the inability to breakdown the lactose sugar (sugar that naturally occurs in the milk of mammals) due to a deficiency of the lactase enzyme. While most infants can digest lactose since their primary source of food is breast milk, they can lose this ability as they get older. Some ethnicities are more prone to lactose intolerance than others. For example, people of African, Asian, Hispanic and Native American descent are more likely to be lactose intolerant.

Other problems with dairy include the hormones and antibiotics used in conventionally raised cows. Additionally, the pasteurization of dairy destroys beneficial enzymes and bacteria that would assist in the digestion of lactose. People who are lactose intolerant can usually still eat cheeses that do not contain the lactose sugar. It is important to determine if you are lactose intolerant or have an allergy to the casein protein found in dairy. Casein is found in all dairy products and may be found in caramel colorings. Below is a helpful guide of where casein is found according to Dr. Fred Pescatore.

DAIRY/CASEIN TO AVOID: Casein is a protein found in milk (cow, buffalo,sheep, goat) and milk products. It is frequently found in soy and vegetarian cheeses. Read the labels. It is found in anything labeled with a "D"

de-lactosed whey	
artificial butter flavor	custard
butter	half and half
buttermilk	hydrolysates
butter flavored oils	lactalbumins
casein/caseinates	lactate/lactic acid
cheese (all types including buffalo,	lactoglobulins
goat and sheep)	lactose
cheese flavoring milk	nougat
cheese food	rennet
churds	whey protein concentrate
cream	whey powder

Following my pregnancy with my second son in my mid-thirties, I didn't feel right. I would get anxiety attacks, heart palpitations and would feel fatigued. My girlfriend Margarita recommended I see her physician, Dr. Robert Pastore, Ph.D., CNS, who is an expert on nutrition, biochemistry and nutrigenomics. He discovered I was gluten intolerant with a blood, urine and saliva test.

Gluten is a protein found in some grains, including wheat. I was told pregnancy can trigger wheat sensitivities. Now I understand how harmful wheat can be to our system. I'm not referring to the wheat of 'yesteryear' that your great grandmother used, but the genetically altered wheat that is used by food manufacturers in bulk at minimal cost. Today's wheat has been sprayed with glyphosate and is genetically different from the ancient Einkorn wheat which had higher protein, less starch and a higher concentration of minerals and carotenoids. Consuming modern wheat gave me elevated blood sugar accompanied by feelings of fatigue that lasted hours.

There is a strong correlation between the use of glyphosate on wheat and the incidence of celiac disease. Glyphosate is an herbicide which is used on many crops in the USA today. It is also important to note the difference between celiac disease and gluten intolerance. One may have gluten intolerance without having the autoantibodies to transglutaminase that would qualify a medical diagnosis of celiac disease.

While breads and pasta obviously contain gluten, you may be surprised to learn that food producers use gluten in foods like soy sauce, imitation meats, ketchup, and ice cream. It is tough to avoid gluten, especially if you eat out frequently. This is why I have laid out a plan for you in this book to help encourage more at-home cooking and food preparation. Gluten can be found in the following list provided by Dr. Fred Pescatore:

Abyssinian hard (wheattriticum duran)
Artificial color
Artificial flavoring
Bagels
Barley grass
Barley malt
Beer
Bleached flour
Blue cheese made with bread
Bran bread
Bread flour
Brewers yeast
Brown flour
Bulgur (wheat/nuts)
Calcium caseinate (contains msg)
Caramel color
Cereal binding
Chilton citric acid
Coloring
Commercial pasta
Couscous
Dextrins
Distilled vinegar
Durum flour
Durum wheat triticum

Edible starch
Einkorn wheat
Farina graham
Filler flavoring
Food starch
Fu (dried wheat gluten)
Germ
Glutamine
Graham flour
Granary flour
Gravy cubes
Groats (barley, wheat)
Gum base
Hard wheat
Hydrolyzed vegetable protein (hpv)
Inulin
Kamut (pasta wheat)
Malt
Malt extract
Malt syrup
Malt flavoring
Malt vinegar
Matzo seminola
Miso mock meats
Modified food starch
Mono & diglycerides

MSG (made outside USA)
Mustard powder
Natural flavoring
Pasta
Pearl barley
Processed meats
Protein tvp
Rice malts (contains barley or koji)
Ready-to-eat cereals
Rye seitan (wheat gluten)
Semolina
Semolina triticum
Shoyue (soy sauce)
Small spelt
Sobo noodles
Sodium caeinate (contains msg)
Soy burgers
Soy sauce
Spelt (triticum spelta)
Sprouted barley
Sprouted wheat
Starch stock cubes
Strong flour
Suet in packets

Tabbouleh
Tamari with meat
Tempeh (fermented soy beans pressed together)
Teriyaki sauce
Textured vegetable
Triicale x tricosecale
Udon (wheat noodle)
Vegetable starch
Vinegars (specific types)
Vital wheat gluten
Vitamin supplement capsules
Wheat, abyssinian hard titicumdurum
Wheat, bulgur
Wheat germ (oil)
Wheat grass (can contain seeds)
Wheat nuts
Wheat starch
Wheat tricum
Wheat triticum mononoccum
Whiskey
Wholemeal flour

Even if you are not celiac or gluten intolerant, eating a more paleo/grain-free diet may improve digestion and gut health. You can substitute with gluten-free grains: amaranth, buckwheat, millet, rice, cassava and even grain-free alternatives like coconut and almond flours if you want to reduce your carbohydrate intake.

Since symptoms of gluten intolerance can be synonymous with symptoms of glyphosate consumption (specifically nutrient deficiencies and alterations in gut microbiota), it is important to source high-quality and organic foods.

Organic should always be non-GMO by default but non-GMO isn't always organic. There are even claims that organic farms can have spillover/contamination from conventional farms.

The gut microbiome imbalances caused by gluten can manifest in the skin. For years I was unaware of my gluten intolerance despite my body's blatant reaction showing up in my skin. Other common symptoms of food sensitivities include fatigue after eating, bloating, gas, constipation, chronic headaches/migraines, heart palpitations, nutrient deficiencies, brain fog, emotional changes and skin reactions. Luckily, the healthier I ate, the more in tune with my body I became. Now that I have been living gluten-free for many years, my life has profoundly improved as well as my energy and mood. I have learned to trust my intuition and want to continue to get the word out. Health starts with education. Best of all, I've been able to pass on the benefits to my children and wish you the same!

If you suspect food allergies, you may benefit from working with a doctor on testing and doing an elimination diet. You can remove common food allergens (dairy, wheat, yeast, eggs, tree nuts, fish, and soy), and anything else you suspect may be triggering a reaction, for two–three weeks. Each food group can be re-introduced one at a time over two or three days to determine which foods are triggering symptoms. It may take you less time to do this if you are already pretty intuitive with your body. Remember, you are your best doctor and your lifestyle and choices are your medicine.

*"Your Body Loves You But
You've Got To Love Your Body"*

Ruth J. Katz

3

A Dog Named Zulu and Discovering a Healthier Me

Rewinding a bit to give you more context of my wellness journey. In 1989, I met the man that would become my husband.

A year later, I decided to train for motherhood by getting my first dog, an African Basenji, who I named Zulu. Never having a dog before, I followed the "pet protocol" and he was given his first vaccination. Something went terribly wrong with his rabies shot and hours later, he became deathly ill. His body started shutting down and I made it to the vet just in time to get him on fluids that saved his life.

My Father and me at my wedding

Over the next few weeks, Zulu broke out in large welts all over his body. He was given steroids and cortisone but nothing was working! I knew I had no choice but to explore alternative ways to help him, which led me to a holistic vet who specialized in homeopathy. Unfamiliar with homeopathy, I quickly learned that it involves treatment with highly diluted substances based on the principles of "like cures like" and the "law of similars" in order to trigger the body's innate healing mechanisms. The speed and effectiveness in which Zulu's health improved post-treatment opened my mind and changed my perspective on medicine and healing.

I started to research everything about homeopathy and other healing modalities. I also examined more closely the foods I was eating, as well as what I was feeding Zulu.

A year later, I got a second Basenji named Poly. She was a retired show dog and the perfect companion to Zulu. I would joke that they both were my best experiments in health as they lived to about 110 in people years. The fact that I controlled what they ate meant they couldn't cheat on their diets. My friends tell me they want to come back reincarnated as my pets because they would be so pampered with organic food, supplements and a holistic cocktails of herbs, vitamins, digestive enzymes, and probiotics. I gave my dogs only filtered water and they had chiropractic care. Although I spent money making sure they were healthy, it paid off in the long run as they never suffered from any illnesses and died naturally of old age.

Zulu and me

About five years into my marriage, we decided it was time to try and get pregnant.

Throughout my trimesters, I ate healthily and exercised. I knew that I wanted to have a natural childbirth with no drugs or medical intervention in a birthing center set up in the hos-

My dogs Zulu and Poly

pital. I chose a midwife as well as a doula, who is a non-medical person that assisted me before, during, and after my son was born.

Before my son was born, I found a wonderful pediatrician named Dr. Mark Nesselson, MD who specializes in integrative medicine. Dr. Nesselson recommended that I take herbs and vitamins before and after my son's birth.

After I breast-fed, I gave my son a hypoallergenic infant formula that contained a predigested protein that virtually eliminates allergic reactions in most babies who are allergic to cow's-milk protein.

Since I am lactose intolerant, I wanted to be cautious with his diet. After the formula, we graduated to homemade almond milk supplemented with fish oil and liquid calcium as well as homemade and purchased organic baby food.

It was important that my son acquired a taste for vegetables before I introduced fruits. Grains were introduced once his digestive system was more developed. I believe in the healing power of spices and flavors they bring to food and made it part of our daily eating ritual to add spices to each dish so that early on, he would experience a wide range of flavors. Exposing children at an early age to a variety of foods enables them to be less picky.

I took a hands-on approach to his diet in his early years. It was harder when he got to preschool as they hosted many bake sales and mothers would bring snacks that were processed and loaded with sugar. Being a working mom didn't help as he often went out with relatives and sitters that weren't following my nutrition protocols. I always made sure there were healthy snacks around and would tell everyone who watched him which foods to avoid and which foods to focus on, but getting them to follow through was a different story.

When my son was in kindergarten, he started to develop eczema and frequently became sick. I learned that his school was serving his class lunch at 10:30 am and since he wasn't hungry enough for lunch, they would give him a bagel or bread and processed cheese sandwich everyday with an artificial fruit drink. The eczema could have been a sign of a food/gluten sensitivity, so I coordinated with the school that he eat lunch without bread and sent him to school with a water bottle so he no longer would drink the artificial fruit juices.

I had another boy a year and a half later. As a baby, my second son was always congested and numerous doctors couldn't figure out the culprit. He was only eating the same pre-digestive infant formula, recommended by my pediatrician that I gave my older son. This formula was chosen because the hydrolyzed protein broken down into smaller parts made it easier to digest in an infant's stomach. Regular cow's milk proteins are larger and can cause excessive crying and fussiness due to indigestion pain. I do not use soy formulas because most are genetically modified and soy has estrogen. It turned out that my second son was allergic to the hydrolyzed protein and needed a different formula. He needed a lactose-free formula with a higher level of choline, which is an ingredient found in breastmilk.

There is a lot of guesswork when it comes to food sensitivities. As a mother, feeding kids becomes a full-time job as you have other diets to look out for aside from your own. As a baby, my second son would scream for his formula or almond milk. He then became very redundant with his words saying "milk momma, milk momma." He then graduated to... "juice mamma, juice mamma." I would give him watered-down pear juice (low potential for causing allergies). When he was older, he moved onto "snack mamma, snack mamma." I would prepare mini ziplock bags of cut organic apples, cut organic carrots, organic chickpeas, seaweed paper, and organic rice crackers. As soon as he could walk, he would come to my bedside in the wee early morning and wake me up and scream loudly in my ear, "I hungry" repeatedly until I would get up and prepare his breakfast. It was enough to drive any mother crazy while simultaneously being appreciative of his appetite! I came to believe that was his favorite line, "I Hungry" (hence, the title of this book). He said it so much that I made him a T-shirt that said "I Hungry." It was such a hit I made a second one saying "I really Hungry" with the lower half of his face on it. My friends found this so hilarious and would say to him, "Kid, are you still hungry?"

He spent his childhood and teenage years endlessly hungry. What's amusing is that he has always been lean and now is muscular and healthy. He has a healthy relationship with food and gravitates towards nourishing choices. I imagine that you reading this means that you want the same for your kids—am I right?

My sons Jonah and Jordan

"Make Wise Choices with Food"

Ruth J. Katz

4

Two Boys Hungry All The Time

Living in Manhattan surrounded by many restaurants, I would often go out to eat with the boys. I discovered a health-conscious restaurant called Candle Cafe (sadly closed now) that became my favorite. My boys came to love this place and got excited everytime we went there. Candle Café proved to me that healthy and organic food can also be tasty and satisfying. The restaurant's founders, Joy Pierson and Bart Potenza, are two of the most lovely people and are also passionate about health.

When Candle Cafe opened, I no longer felt like an outsider when dining out! Finally, there was a place that served food from the freshest local ingredients available. I am not vegan, but I appreciate the attention to quality of ingredients. They are responsible for bringing sophistication to vegetarian cuisine, not to mention the concepts of local, seasonal, sustainable, and vegan into the culinary mainstream. Check out their cookbooks, *The Candle Café Cookbook* and *Candle 79 Cookbook*. I refer to them often when making healthy tasty meals.

One of my favorite sayings is "Everyday is a new day to start again." I believe that no matter what your family eats now or has eaten in the past, you can always make improvements. When I found a restaurant that believed in my philosophy that there are better substitute foods and tasty cuisine, it confirmed I was on the right track. My kids didn't even realize they were eating well. They were eating the whole foods they had been exposed to from the beginning of their lives: nutrient dense and loaded with vitamins. I live by the rule "eat as close to natural as possible with real food from the earth."

How many times have you heard if you can't pronounce it, skip it? That is how I look at labels. Food labels have been required by law since 1990. Food manufactures must usually list every ingredient contained in their products. However, there are exceptions. For example, foods served at restaurants with less than 20 locations do not have to disclose ingredients. I discovered this while on vacation with two other families and their seven kids. For five days straight, I watched them drink unlimited amounts of soda and choose tons of starches like pizza and fries even though some had pre-existing health conditions. There was a wonderful buffet with all kinds of healthy choices like salads, fruits and fish, yet the parents didn't encourage their kids to choose healthy options. Without being able to read the labels on the food offered, I opted to go the healthy route: fresh fruits, vegetables, salads, fish and meats that were not fried. We are a country with a growing prevalence of obesity, with the rate of obesity in children (2–19 years old) at 22.4% in 2020 compared to 19.3% in 2019.

Based on false marketing claims, Americans thought switching to margarine and vegetable oil would be better for them by avoiding the saturated fat in butter. Margarine and vegetable oils tend to have trans fats and also contain a disproportionately high amount of omega 6: omega 3 fatty acids, which can cause inflammation, obesity, and metabolic diseases related to insulin resistance such as type II diabetes. In fact 88–90% of Americans have some form of metabolic dysfunction or insulin resistance and the prevalence of vegetable oils like soybean oil in processed foods is a contributor. Early human ancestors ate a ratio of 1:1 omega 6: omega 3 because the only fats consumed were those of whole animal foods or coconut. Once industrialized seed oils replaced butter, the ratio in the modern standard American diet is now 20:1 omega 6: omega 3's. Polyunsaturated fats are also less chemically stable than saturated fats and lead to oxidative and free-radical damage, which harms cells, mitochondria, and DNA.

Saturated fats are more chemically stable because they only have single bonds, and fats like butter also contain fat-soluble vitamins such as vitamin A and vitamin k2 that are beneficial for growing kids which protect the arteries from calcification that leads to atherosclerosis and heart disease. The main issue with these vegetable oils is that they are hidden in what many people consider to be "health foods," from light salad dressing, whole grain bread, mayonnaise, condiments, sauces, hummus, protein bars, and more. Fried food is almost always fried in these oils, making them even more harmful! The trick is to make your own salad dressings, sauces, and condiments from scratch, and read labels carefully.

Stick to saturated fats from coconut oil or monounsaturated fats like olive oil. The below chart guides you to which oils to avoid (in red) and which ones to use (in green). The more linoleic acid, the more likely it is to cause oxidative damage and inflammation.

Type of Oil	Type of Fat	Linoleic Acid
Sunflower Oil	Polyunsaturated Fat	68%
Corn Oil	Polyunsaturated Fat	59%
Cottonseed Oil	Polyunsaturated Fat	54%
Soybean Oil	Polyunsaturated Fat	51%
Peanut Oil	Polyunsaturated Fat	32%
Canola Oll	Polyunsaturated Fat	20%
Extra Virgin Olive Oil	Monounsaturated Fat	10%
Fat Pasture raised Lard	Monounsaturated Fat	10%
Cocoa Butter	Saturated Fat	3%
Grass-fed Ghee	Saturated Fat	3%
Grass Fed Butter	Saturated Fat	2%
Coconut Oil	Saturated Fat	2%
Macadamia Nut Oil	Monounsaturated Fat	2%

Chart by Lexi Abi Khattar MS, https://www.nutritionin2ition.com/

As if you didn't need more reasons to avoid processed foods, other hidden and potentially harmful ingredients include: BHA, nitrates, sulfites, benzoates, and food colorings. What I am trying to reiterate here is get in the habit of reading labels, as boring as it is—it could enhance your life! Additionally, the more whole foods you stick to that do not require labels (eggs for example), the better. While on the subject of whole foods, it is essential to source high-quality fruits and vegetables and choose organic when necessary.

The dirty dozen and the clean fifteen are what the Environmental Working Group (EWG) ranks from collected tests on over 96,000 pesticide residues in produce from the USDA and FDA. Based on this, they created rankings of the "Dirty Dozen," the fruits and vegetables most likely to contain pesticides when grown conventionally and our friends the "Clean Fifteen," those who carry the least pesticides. They can be found at organic local farm stands.

Dirty Dozen List 2023

Always buy Organic

1. Strawberries
2. Spinach
3. Kale, mustard greens, collard greens
4. Nectarines
5. Apples
6. Grapes
7. Cherries
8. Peaches
9. Pears
10. Bell & Hot peppers
11. Celery
12. Tomatoes

Clean Fifteen List 2023

(lower pesticide content)

1. Avocados
2. Sweet corn
3. Pineapple
4. Onions
5. Papaya
6. Sweet peas
7. Eggplant
8. Asparagus
9. Broccoli
10. Cabbage
11. Kiwi
12. Cauliflower
13. Mushrooms
14. Honeydew
15. Cantaloupe

While not everything is in our control, we can control what we buy and feed our families. Due to high prevalence of cancer and other diseases, we need to be mindful of what we are putting in our bodies. I make sure that my kitchen is filled with all good staples and healthy food choices. Please refer to Part Three: Food Shopping List.

Kids can say they are hungry twenty minutes after you've fed them. Regardless of whether or not they have already eaten, I guarantee they will come up with an excuse to express their hunger. I recommend you have some quick, healthy and appealing foods that you can prepare like grilled organic chicken breast with organic roasted vegetables. You can make this faster than it takes to order takeout and get it delivered! The upside is you can control what goes into this fast but tasty meal. In fact, start cooking in bulk so that you have enough for leftovers. It also helps if you take some time each week to prepare veggies that are washed, cut and ready to be cooked. Planning the foods you feed you and your kids will also save you time in the long run. I hope I have inspired you to start changing the way you buy and prepare food!

A rule became that my kids got to have a piece of cake at a party as long as they had filled up on a healthy breakfast or lunch. It made them less likely to crave unhealthy foods. When I hosted birthday parties, I was creative with food presentations, and made the food aesthetically appealing as well as healthy and tasty. I always made sure that there were fruit and vegetable trays for snacking with a dip of protein rich-hummus (homemade since store bought hummus is made with PUFA (polyunsaturated fatty acid) or vinai-

My sons Jordan and Jonah

grette and I replaced those sugary sodas with bubbly mineral water or natural fruit infused water. This is also a great opportunity to get the kids involved by creating a taco bar or a salad bar as part of the fun and let them assemble their own healthy plates.

Parties and social outings became easier for my boys to navigate, because they learned how to make healthy choices. The healthy foundation that I provided them enabled them to grow to their optimal weight, while their food sensitivities subsided and any other conditions thankfully disappeared.

Now they have stamina and clear minds to study and learn. By giving my family healthy food choices, I watched my sons become healthy young men. Now they equate what they eat with how they feel. What more could a parent ask for?

"Educate Yourself And Try New Foods"

Ruth J. Katz

My son Jonah

5

Finding The Balanced Diet

There is no reason for a child to ever feel deprived post meal as long as they eat nutrient-dense foods, high-quality proteins, carbs and fats at each meal and snack. It is also important that they are properly hydrated and are getting enough micronutrients and electrolytes. If you teach them from a young age the importance of nutrition and how it impacts their growth and development, you will be rewarded with them asking for water instead of soda, and for apples and carrots instead of fruit roll-ups and goldfish crackers.

It shocks me to know how many kids today don't consume enough nutrient-dense whole foods. The majority of kids today eat highly processed, chemically altered foods. A balanced diet of proteins such as pasture-raised poultry, wild fish, pasture-raised meats and eggs (and even well-soaked and prepared organic lentils to diminish lectin content) are high-quality proteins to fuel your growing children. Teaching them the essential role that protein plays in growing bones and muscle will motivate them to want this essential nutrient.

The quality and source of protein should be taken into account when navigating through the grocery store. Below is a guide on how to choose your proteins. It is best to buy proteins from a trusted butcher, farm or a grocery store with organic options. Below are key terms to note.

Pasture-raised soy- and corn-free eggs. This means the hens have space to roam free and eat what they find outside like worms, grass and other things they can find in the dirt/soil. Free-range means that the hens have some space but may still be eating GMO corn and soy feed.

Dairy. Products from the milk of A2 cows that are 100% grass fed, or goats. If you can eat dairy, raw milk contains beneficial enzymes that help with digestion.

Meats. 100% grass-fed, organic. If you aren't buying this type of meat, you risk buying meat that is raised conventionally with hormones, antibiotics and GMO feed.

Pasture-raised chicken, poultry and ham. Soy and Corn Free. Chicken tends to be higher in PUFA fat than grass-fed beef so it is important that you get good-quality poultry to optimize omega 6: omega 3 ratios and avoid hormones and antibiotics.

Wild-caught fish. Farm raised fish is usually fed GMO soy while wild caught is more nutrient dense in omega 3 fatty acids and eats their natural diet.

Animal proteins have a higher conversion to tissue/muscle than plant proteins, specifically dairy and eggs. In traditional and ancient cultures, they had wisdom of preparing and cooking foods optimally so they would be beneficial for our gut health. This is why it is important to prepare plant foods in a way that diminishes their toxin content. You also want to make sure to buy organic since conventionally raised plants are loaded with pesticides that cannot be removed via washing.

Negotiating with your children, for example, saying to them "just a few more bites", or "if you eat your vegetables, you'll get dessert" is only a temporary fix. Children who learn to make deals about eating, quickly learn to make deals and ask for rewards for doing other things. Soon they won't do anything without a reward.

I understood early on that I could raise my sons in a contained little world, but there were going to be outside forces at play. Restaurants can be a huge challenge, especially family-oriented ones. I have come to the conclusion that there is no such thing as "kid food." Food is food. Special kids menus, with cute drawings on them often limit choices to things like chicken fingers and french fries, macaroni and cheese, hot dogs, grilled cheese sandwiches, pizza, hamburgers, spaghetti, and soda and ice cream. What is "kid food?" Does it exist entirely apart from adult cuisine? If we think about it, why aren't kids eating what we eat, just in different portions? In fact, kids that are growing with faster metabolisms may need bigger portions (depending on age) than adults who are no longer growing. We don't need kid menus; rather, we need different portions (depending on the age). Kids need healthy fats that help them to absorb fat-soluble vitamins A, D, E and K. Even some minerals require that fat be in the diet for proper absorption.

Often, foods marketed towards kids are fried and contain high levels of omega 6 fats, chemicals, hormones, GMOs, nitrates, high-fructose corn syrup and other names for added sugar. If I ate these kinds of foods, I would get fat and bloated, not to mention cranky, irritable, and unproductive.

People can be lazy when it comes to making food choices and I've been guilty of this when I've been too tired to cook. Discovering new foods and flavors is one of the most family-friendly ways to bond with your kids. Many times on Saturday mornings, the boys will want something different from one another, so my rule is that we eat the same thing with the exception that if they are willing to prepare and make their own breakfast.

One of the most valuable concepts I learned from the Institute for Integrative Nutrition was the "crowding-out theory." This theory is an effective way to avoid habitual consumption of unhealthy food when restrictive behavior fails (and it usually fails). The principle of crowding-out suggests that you focus on adding healthy foods and nutrients to your diet, instead of focusing on restricting foods. By adding healthy whole foods, you will "crowd out" the unhealthy foods because you will feel satiated without feeling deprived. I used this concept with my kids, and their satiety with healthy foods and lack of cravings for unhealthy foods proves that it works. If you fill the body with healthy, nutrient-dense food, it is only natural that cravings for unhealthy foods will lessen substantially.

Each choice towards a whole food before choosing a processed food takes your kids one step closer to eating better. You are simply making less room for a day of eating poorly. Once you crowd out the unhealthy choices, you'll find that your kids will crave them less. Changing how you eat happens one choice at a time.

Below are my favorite healthy foods that I recommend in a fast food world:

- Pasture-raised organic chicken strips with peanut sauce and shaved carrot salad (Thai style)
- Hard-boiled pasture-raised eggs with raw carrots and sliced apple (snack)
- Fresh, grilled, or baked fish with roasted carrots and green goddess avocado sauce (Wild, not farmed.)
- Grass-fed burger with baked sweet potato fries
- Zucchini noodles with shrimp or organic chicken
- Colorful Salad with choice of protein with avocado dressing (Recipes in Resource section at the back of this book)

As a parent, it was so important that I became aware of the direct influence foods would have on my boy's health and development. I learned a lot from Dr. Fred Pescatore, who is a traditionally trained physician whose private practice specializes in integrative medicine. He uses in the ALCAT Test that measures food sensitivities, which helps him personalize and customize diet plans for his patients. ("People are sometimes shocked when they get the test results back and then they don't believe it", says Dr. Pescatore.) I learned from him how food has an impact on my children's health as well as their behavior.

Keep in mind that no two bodies are alike and the human body is dynamic, meaning different foods may work better for people at different times in their lives. After the results of the ALCAT Test, I eliminated certain foods from my boys' diet. There is a reason why there is an old adage about food: "You are what you eat." You are actually more what you absorb. Processed foods can irritate the intestinal barrier and lead to leaky gut syndrome, which can manifest as allergies and skin conditions. Your children's diet influences their gut microbiome, where neurotransmitters are synthesized, affecting their mental well-being and ability to concentrate and focus.

Once I understood that everything my children consumed became part of them, my life changed. Think of it as building a house from the ground up. The body's strength and resilience comes from diet. A sturdy foundation becomes a strong force against life's storms. Without that solid frame, how can your child grow up to be a healthy and thriving reflection of you? Preventing a lifetime of obesity, allergies, asthma, behavioral issues and diabetes is your responsibility, and it's time for you to take charge. I suggest to track your food intake for 14 to 30 days to see which foods are repeated too often and which types of nutrients are lacking. It helps everyone to understand how the foods they are eating are affecting their bodies as well as figuring out how to maintain a healthier diet. You can use an application of your choice to keep track of what is being eaten, including snacks and drinks, and be sure to report if there is any unusual reaction to a food. If so, do not repeat the same food for four days. Food molecules need time to clear the body from overload. It can take around 23 days for the proteins in our immune system (antibodies) to turn over.

Roger Deutsch, the coauthor of "Your Hidden Food Allergies Are Making You Fat," says if you put the wrong food into the body, you can disrupt any real metabolic and physical function and produce inflammation in any part of the body." I am a big believer on having a wide variety in the diet and rotating foods in order to optimize nutrient intake. I find that many people are creatures of habit and eat the same foods out of convenience. My advice is to step out of your comfort zone and try new recipes so you are getting a variety of nutrients. Try lunch foods for breakfast and explore foods from different cultures. There is a whole world of different types of food. Be open and expand your horizons and palate.

Remember these tips:

- Prepackaged, processed food is a fast track to obesity.
- Focus on crowding out the bad foods by adding in satiating nutrient-dense whole foods.
- Make sure to focus on quality and source your foods well.
- Meals and snacks should be balanced with high-quality proteins, carbs and fats.

"Take Your Time To Enjoy Your Meals"

Ruth J. Katz

My son Jonah

6

It's All In The Presentation

I found it easier to feed my kids when I made food fun and aesthetically appealing. Kids are delighted by what their eyes see and believe me, their appetite will follow suit without question! I love using Japanese Bento boxes because of their organized compartments, which teaches portion control at an early age. There are a number of companies that sell Bento box lunchboxes. We use dinner plates from a company called Fred's Food Face Plates that have faces of men or women, so the kids can decorate the face with food.

Other favorite helpful tools have been different-shaped ice cube trays. Fred's makes some fun ones with skulls. You can fill them with natural juices or coconut milk. Another hit is a sushi roller to make rolls with rice, vegetables, fruits, meats, and fish. We also love our food dehydrator as we cut up different fruits and vegetables and let them dehydrate overnight into dried fruit snacks.

I find that kids love little baggies filled with snacks. I fill ziplock bags with organic carrots, seaweed, turkey slices, and dried fruits and nuts. I also use mini utensils that you get at party good stores. It's not always easy getting children to try foreign foods. That is why presentation is everything. Sharing the preparation and planning of meals with your kids will not only be exciting, but also educational in teaching them the process of a healthy lifestyle. If they are old enough, they can start using cooking tools. My kids like using avocado, banana and apple slicers as well as lemon and orange squeezers. For a great natural dessert, we use a device called Yonanas that makes a frozen dessert out of frozen bananas or other frozen fruits. We make toppings with shaved coconut, sliced almonds, raw cacao, raw honey and hemp, chia or flax seeds.

Lately, we have been making healthier desserts with fun baking trays called cake pops. We use cake mixes made from organic coconut or almond flour and we add vanilla extract, coconut milk, honey and semi-sweet dark chocolates or blueberries. The cake comes out like a lollipop and we add sticks. We also experiment with fun shaped muffin and cupcake molds. There is a cool skull-shaped mold at Williams-Sonoma.

Here is a list of our favorite gadgets:

- skewer sticks
- orange or lemon squeezer
- cake pop mold
- pizza cutter
- rolling pin
- bento boxes
- sushi roller
- smorgasbord plates
- kids' chopsticks
- fun shaped cookie cutters
- fun shaped cake molds
- fun shaped ice cube trays
- Beaba baby food maker
- mason jars
- fruit baller
- banana slicer
- apple cutter
- cupcake maker
- infused water bottles
- NutriBullet
- Magic Bullet
- fun ice cube trays
- instant slushi maker
- popsicle molds
- straws
- avocado slicer
- egg cutter
- colorful squirting tubes
- magic veggie twister
- Yonanas frozen dessert maker
- Fred's plate line
- popcorn maker
- fruit dehydrator

It is fun to make art with food. There are great recipes at www.food.com.

Making fruit and vegetable animals can be fun for kids. The best part about fun fruits and vegetables is they are loaded with vitamins and antioxidants. You can make platters with a theme such as fruit sushi by cutting up fruit and putting it on top of rice.

- Make up some colorful fruit kabobs for snack time. You can use wooden or metal skewers. Rinse fruit with cool water, slide strawberries, grapes, blueberries, banana pieces, orange slices, and raspberries onto each skewer.
- I love to mix up a fruit salad and have the kids learn to eat it with chopsticks.

- Remember cutting out interesting designs from cantaloupes and other melons are easier compared to other fruits so I use them a lot when doing fruit designs. You can find special fruit-cutting tools to create flowers, stars, and other shapes in most stores.

Create kid-friendly designs using different pieces of fruit. Things You'll Need:

- Fruit/veggies
- Any food you have
- Cutting tools

- Skewers
- Chop sticks
- Toothpicks

Use fruit/veggies/meat to make pigs, cats, or dogs:

1. Use turkey/apple slices for the face, ears and nose
2. Use olive slices for the eyes and eyebrows and mouth
3. Use some ketchup for cheeks
4. Get creative with the foods you have

Make a clown face using fruit:

1. A pepper top for the head
2. A banana/orange slice for the mouth
3. Orange and berries for the eyes
4. Cherry and bell pepper combo for the bowtie
5. Bell peppers and apple slices for the ears

Make animal faces on different types of breakfast toasts:

1. A prune or almond for the nose
2. Sliced strawberry for the ears
3. Banana slices for the eyes and nose base
4. Berries for the eyes

5. Use different spreads such as nut butter, avocado, or jam spreads to make the base and gluten-free toast
6. Get creative

Make a face from your eggs:
1. Use eggs cooked in peppers as eyes.
2. Olive for the nose
3. Carrots/sweet potatoes for the mouth
4. Lettuce for the mustache

Make a puppy or mouse from pancakes and fruit:
1. Use pancakes for the face and ears
2. Use some nut butter to decorate the face (nose area)
3. Use raspberries for the nose and mouth
4. Use blueberries for the eyes with sliced banana for the eyelids
5. Sprinkle coconut for the hair

Make a lion using a combo of veggies and fruits:
1. Sliced apple or potatoes for the body and face and carve out certain areas for the nose/paws/tail
2. Gluten-free pasta or shaved carrots for the lion's mane and tail
3. Peas for the eyes

Make breakfast pudding look like a bunny:
1. Chia seed pudding or coconut yogurt parfait as the face
2. Blueberries for eyes & nose
3. Apple slices for ears
4. Coconut flakes for whiskers

Make a bear out of fruit:
1. Sliced green apple or kiwi for the face and body
2. Grapes for the eyes
3. Carve grapes for the nose/mouth/ears

Making fun and whimsical food presentations can help a child try something new. Gently teach them the necessary nutritional information through clever presentation that makes food fun! By working with them to stick to a healthy lifestyle, they will one day pass this on to their children.

"The First Wealth Is Health"

Ralph Waldo Emerson

7

The Family That Eats Together Bonds Together

When it comes to the eating habits of children, Quality mealtime is desperately needed. We live in a world of overcrowded classes, television, texting, video games, and surfing the web. It re-wires their ability to practice important social skills, like listening to others and having an opinion. My kids naturally fight, as boys often do. I have found that the more we have meals together, the more they would work through their disagreements. Sitting down to regular meals with your family is also a good opportunity to practice some mindful eating tips which can help prevent overeating at meals.

The following are some of them:

- Appreciate the food and company.
- Put utensils down while chewing food.
- Chew food thoroughly before swallowing to ensure digestive enzymes in saliva start breaking down the food.
- Eat until your 80% full or what the Japanese like to call "hara hachi bu."

Sitting down and connecting with your child at least five times a week will build a lifetime of social skills. Tests have proved that children that have a regular meal routine with their parents excel in almost all aspects of their life from higher grades in school, to maintaining loving, healthy relationships, to staying healthy, safe and out of trouble. Family meals are possible regardless of family structure (one-or two-parent homes). Studies have shown that this family time and structure may minimize the likelihood of drug abuse and behavioral problems in the future.

Our nation's drug problem is not going to be solved by legislation; "It's going to be solved across the kitchen table" said Joseph Califano, the former US Secretary of Health. Years of research has led Califano to the conclusion that parents still have the strongest influence on kids. "I call the ages ten to twenty the killer decade," he says. "That's when drugs and alcohol rear their ugly heads, and the family dinner falls apart, just when it's most important."

Unlike when I was growing up, parents these days have to deal with the overload of instant gratification and technology. Between the TV, texting, cell phones, video games, and social media, kids today spend at least seven and a half hours a day using some form of electronic media. All of this is interfering with us as parents from staying engaged in their lives, not to mention any outdoor playtime and connecting with nature. I'm just as guilty of allowing the overuse of electronics, but it can come with a big fat price tag down the road, so I try to limit it. People are more likely to mindlessly snack while watching TV. Family dinners are a deterrent to unhealthy eating habits. Nutrition expert Ellyn Satter says, "Meals are as essential for nurturing as they are for nutrition. Meals provide us all with reliable access to food and they provide children with dependable access to their parents. Without meals, a home is just a place to stay."

Don't you think it's time we got it right? Having the kids involved in all aspects of eating, from the shopping, the preparation, setting the table, sitting down and enjoying a family meal, and the clean-up synergistically work to create lifelong lessons they will pass on to their future children.

One of my favorite books The Family Dinner by Laurie David has ten steps, or rules, that have been the key success to her family dinners:

- STEP ONE: It's a date. Set a regular time for the family dinner.
- STEP TWO: Everyone comes to the table at the same time. No late stragglers and no showing up when you feel like it.
- STEP THREE: No phones. Do not answer the phone at dinner. Do not bring an electronic device or a toy to the table.
- STEP FOUR: One meal, no substitutions.
- STEP FIVE: Everyone tries everything. Tasting everything is an important rule. It shows respect to whoever prepared the food and respect for yourself.
- STEP SIX: No television. Of course, that includes any electronic device.
- STEP SEVEN: Water only. No individual plastic bottles allowed in the kitchen. Serve it cold and preferably from a reverse-osmosis filtered tap in a clear glass pitcher or bottle.

- STEP EIGHT: Friends and family welcome. I always encourage my kids to invite their friends and even their friends' parents to dinner.
- STEP NINE: You're excused. No one leaves the table until after everyone is finished with their meal.
- STEP TEN: Everyone helps with clean-up.

No exceptions. It's more fun and clean-up is faster when everyone chips in. I know how hard getting the family to sit down to dinner can be and I've got two active boys. Standing and eating at the kitchen counter isn't the answer. This can lead to overeating, and not always making the right healthy choices. When you're standing, you don't really enjoy what you're eating, but simply stuff your face.

Mealtime doesn't have to be just your immediate family. You can mix it up with friends and their children. Don't be afraid to be creative. Fun meals don't always have to be dinner—they can also be a Saturday breakfast, or a late afternoon snack, or even healthy takeout when you're not in the mood to cook. An outing to a restaurant can mix things up and make the kids feel like it's an adventure. I've been giving my kids suggestions of what to order since they were old enough to go out to restaurants. They kid around about ordering unhealthy foods, but rarely follow through with it. My go-to foods when we are out are organic vegetables, eggs, avocado, grass-fed lamb chops and steak and wild-caught fish. You can make ordering healthy food fun and make your kids feel they have control in their decisions by giving them options. For example, you can ask them "would you prefer the grass-fed lamb chops with a side of roasted carrots or the shrimp, mango and avocado salad?"

On another note, I suggest vetting restaurants or takeout places that you frequently visit: ask them what types of oils they use, where they source their meat and if they use organic produce. If you live in a kid-friendly area, get to know the people around you. Invite them over for a healthy potluck or buffet dinner. It will feel like a party for the kids. These mealtimes are meant for catching up and really getting to know your kids as they start to have thoughts and ideas of their own. Use these evenings as an opportunity to share family history. Studies show that kids who knew a lot about their family history learned it around the dinner table.

Dinner doesn't just involve eating together. It also includes shopping and preparing the meals, as well as cleaning up together afterwards. I've always loved serving family style from platters and bowls. Allowing kids to serve themselves gives them a sense of control and independence. By getting them involved from start to finish, they learn that I'm not the sole chef/server/ busboy/dishwasher. Of course, it isn't always possible to get the family to sit down four nights a week. Many parents are now at work during meals, when a generation ago they would have been eating dinner together every night.

"Having Great Health Is Euphoric"

Ruth J. Katz

My brother Jason and his son Ben

8

Expanding the Palate of Picky Eaters

W hen my boys were one and two years old, I left my career in the mort-gage business. Mothering is challenging at best and becoming a full-time stay-at-home mom can become an overwhelming task that requires your undivided attention. I had a new full-time job that was 24 hours, seven days a week: being a mom. Life centered around food and care for my kids. Thank goodness I had set in motion an "after-school-snack" and "homework-before-dinner" routine that my boys consistently followed. There is a place and time for everything and kids depend on a daily plan. Shown the way, they will follow from your example.

It's important to be firm but not preachy when getting kids to try some-thing new and to help them feel personally responsible for their choices. A good example is getting your kids to choose and make their own healthy lunches for school by suggesting something new at least once a week. Being raised on healthy choices had always been a way of life for them, so involving them in the process made them confident and comfortable in trying new things.

In nursery school when it was our turn to bring snacks for the class, I would always get my boys involved in choosing what to bring. We made healthy choices like fresh organic fruit, organic dried fruits, seaweed paper, organic cut carrots and celery. I was known as "the best snack mom!" The fact that my kids participated in the selection and preparation sets a precedent at a young age that they will one day pass on to their children.

Your eating habits and food choices will ultimately influence your chil-dren's food preferences. This is not a big surprise, since we are more likely to actually prepare the foods we enjoy. Familiarity with foods is important for children. At first, my boys were picky and often times, I found myself frus-trated. I slowly started to win them over with a wide range of healthy recipes and by preparing meals together. I learned that my boys were less likely to try something new if I hadn't tasted it first myself! If you tend to be a picky eater, your children may imitate your behavior.

If you offer several healthy choices (including the ones they like) at each meal, they will be more agreeable to trying new foods. You should also frequently add in a new type of food. Statistically, children need to be offered a new food as many as 15 times before they will eat it. With picky eaters, it's often about control. Most kids prefer to feed themselves rather than be fed. Prepare finger foods they can hold as this makes them feel in control. Let

My sons Jordan and Jonah

them decide where the food goes on the plate: carrots here, salmon there. If you let your children serve themselves, they feel involved. What I learned as a parent is that kids need to express their free will.

They are used to being told what to do all day, so if you give them the illusion that they are in control with food choices, they are more likely to adapt healthy habits. The two things you can't force them to do are eat and sleep. It is important to respect their independence.

Giving my kids choices allows them to feel empowered. The foods in my pantry and refrigerator are to my standards, so whatever they choose is acceptable. My boys are so active that they don't want to sit for long. I always set their meals out before they sit down and let them get up when they are finished. Often, kids have trouble with the texture of mushy food. If that's the case, try to offer them apple slices instead of applesauce, or a baked potato instead of mashed. The best way to get them to enjoy mushy food is to combine it with crunchy food that they like. I refuse to become a slave in the kitchen by preparing special meals for each of my boys, and I always include something they know and like on their plate. I also include healthy 'dips' like hummus and natural salad dressing to encourage them to eat fruits and vegetables. We call it "dippity do."

It is normal for kids to be wary of unfamiliar foods. The technical term for this behavior, which usually peaks between the ages of 2 and 6, is food neophobia. It can be frustrating, to say the least. So what causes it? In part, us parents do, both biologically and psychologically. In a 2007 study, Lucy Cooke, a psychologist and public health scientist at the University College London compared the eating characteristics of a group of fraternal twins with those of their parents. The same study was done with a group of identical twins and their parents. Cooke calculated that about 78% of the population-wide variation in food neophobia severity is explained by genetic differences. In other words, food neophobia is a heritable trait. Moral of the story is to always lead by example by eating in front of your kids what you would want them to eat.

What I've learned is that if you put pressure on your kids, it builds stress, which they in turn associate with the particular food they are being told to eat. The last thing you want to do is intimidate them into being afraid to eat in front of you out of fear you won't approve. If you can get it past them, try a food like avocado for the 15th time and you may win them over. I would stay away from bribery using a cookie as a reward for eating healthy, because they will associate that food as a negative thing and a cookie as being a reward and positive thing!

Mealtime together should be a positive experience. Instead of "Eat your vegetables," try "Aren't your vegetables tasty?" Make sure you always serve familiar foods with new, unknown foods so they are more willing to try something new. If nutrition is a challenging topic in your house, you are not alone! Until your child's food preferences mature, consider the following tips for preventing mealtime battles recommended by the Mayo Clinic:

No. 1: Respect your child's appetite—or lack of one. Don't force food on your kids when they're not hungry! Bribing your child to eat or clean their plate can lead to negative connotations around food. Serve small portions to avoid overwhelming your child and give them the opportunity to independently ask for more, and more than likely they will.

No. 2: Stick to a routine. Serve meals and snacks at about the same time daily. Provide water or fresh juice with their meals instead of in between meals to avoid decreasing their appetite.

No. 3: Be patient with new foods. Repeated exposure to a new food is helpful. My boys would touch or smell new foods and put tiny bits in their mouths and then take them back out again. Encourage your child by talking about a food's color, shape, aroma and texture, not whether it tastes good. Serve new foods along with their favorites.

No. 4: Make it Fun. I love turning veggies and fruits into fun shapes with cookie cutters. Esthetic presentations will encourage kids to eat healthy foods. Offer breakfast foods for dinner and remember to add a variety of brightly colored foods.

No. 5: Recruit your child's help. Get your kids involved in selecting the fruits, veggies and other healthy foods. Encourage them to rinse veggies, stir batter or set the table.

No. 6: Set a good example. I've lived by this rule since the boys were young: if you eat a variety of healthy foods, your children will likely follow suit.

No. 7: Be creative. Add diced broccoli or shredded carrots to spaghetti sauce. Top cereal with fruit slices or mix a grated zucchini and carrots into casseroles, soups, and stews.

No. 8: Minimize distraction. During mealtime. I turn off the TV and other electronics. This creates a calm and soothing atmosphere to help your kids digest their food properly.

No. 9: Don't offer dessert as a reward. Withholding dessert sends the message that dessert is this desirable "hidden treasure." I allow them to have a healthy dessert once or twice a week such as frozen fruit or homemade healthy fudge pops.

No. 10: Food log for picky eaters. If picky eating is compromising your child's growth and development, consult your child's physician. Keep a food diary and notice which foods are in excess and which could be added.

"*Trust Your Instincts*"

Ruth J. Katz

Photo taken by my son Jonah

9

On My Own and Balancing a Healthy Diet in a Divorced Household

In my early forties I wound up getting divorced. With my children being my priority, I wanted to make the transition as smooth as possible. Food and a healthy, balanced diet, played a huge part of our daily interaction. I wanted to make sure that they were getting the same healthy choices in food and snacks when they were at my ex-husband's house.

I've tried my best to educate my family and babysitters on the foods that we eat and the foods that we avoid. I've found that most of the time when I'm not there to supervise their food intake, the sitters will often times give in and let them have whatever they want. That is called the path of least resistance. However, I've outsmarted them, as there are only healthy choices in my refrigerator and pantry.

When my marriage ended, my kids divided their time between my house and my ex-husband's. I felt relieved when my kids told me their father buys mom-approved food. It's my mission when it comes to the boys to do the right thing, and I've made it a habit of food shopping as a family since the boys were little. Not only did they see my healthy choices going into the shopping cart, but they were more engaged in the process, asking questions about food and learning along the way.

I may be a single mom, but I'm not raising my kids alone. Between their grandparents and many friends, they have a constant, loving and nurturing environment. When the parents live separately, the most ideal parent–child relationships are when the parents continue to cooperate effectively. This is not always easy, but imperative for the well-being of your children.

The learning curve for us parents is how we can improve from our mistakes. Two homes, and one family isn't ideal, but it can work, especially if both sides are willing to proceed in the best interest of their children, and reach compromises. Divorces can affect children emotionally, so we worked together to create loving and safe havens for our kids.

"Eat When Hungry, Sleep When Tired"

The Little Rascals

My sons Jonah and Jordan

10

Everything In Its Place

My outside appearance is very social and I enjoy material things, but my authenticity and passions revolve around health, nutrition, environmental causes, and animals. My body is very sensitive and I have had to navigate my inner wisdom and research to find what is best for me. I like to call myself a "tree hugger in high heels." Since I am social and attend many parties, charity events and dinners, I often times get asked why I'm not eating something. I know there are hidden ingredients in prepared foods beyond my control, and I have to be careful not to consume something that may trigger a reaction. As I've gotten older, I try to not make a huge deal about my infatuation with ingredients; however, people seem to be intrigued by my questions and choices, inspiring them to want to learn more and improve their health.

I typically wind up being the "preacher of all things healthy" at social gatherings or at dinner tables. It's not like I intentionally do this, but a question will get started and soon more and more people become involved in the conversation and they focus on what I am saying about food, diet, and health. The information available to us is always changing and what's good for one person may not work for another. I believe that everyone has a unique bio-individuality and you have to experiment to find out what works best for you. The human body is dynamic and even among the same person, different foods may work better at different life stages based on physiological and environmental changes.

It's amazing how far I have come to where I am now. Being a single parent, there are times it is more convenient to grab a salad or packaged sushi rather than preparing a homemade meal. But eating on the fly happens to the best of us in the hectic world we live in, so don't beat yourself up if you can't always prepare and sit down to a fresh, home-cooked meal.

Adjusting your diet throughout your life is a continuous process. Eliminating specific foods when you're having a physical reaction will help you pinpoint those foods that are causing the problem. The key is listening to your body.

Nobody ever said child rearing is easy. After years of raising my sons into young adults, I am currently reaping the benefits of their strong cognitive and muscular development, a proud mother to say the least. The effort I lived and breathed from before they were in the womb until now has paid off, as the foundation was set at an early age and their palates for healthy food can guide them and their future children. As long as you instill in your children the importance of acts of kindness and good habits combined with their ability to make great food choices that fuel their bodies as well as their minds, then I would say they are well on their road to wellness of body, spirit, and mind.

PART II

Food And Other Great Things

"We Are What We Eat.
Everything We Put Inside Us Becomes Part Of Us
And Breaks Down Into Our Blood System And
Becomes Our Cells"

Ruth J. Katz

11

Let's Get In the Kitchen

Funny enough, one of our family's favorite pastimes is food shopping. Although that may not sound so fun for kids, we have made it an enjoyable process. I believe in a hands-on approach: get the kids in the kitchen, and let them play with the pots and pans. Take them to the grocery store with you and let them help you make healthy choices. I found when my boys knew what was on the menu, they were more able to adapt. If you make the time to engage your children in fun and playful conversation about food, they will soon be making suggestions of things they want to try. One of the best ways to make this happen is not by explaining, as much as by involving them in their healthy food selections. Remember to keep it positive and get everybody excited on this journey.

One of the ways I found to get my boys interested was to let them plan and choose a meal once or twice a week. Don't drive yourself crazy by making different foods for each child, as it is confusing and sends the wrong message. I made sure I set a precedent that as a family, we would eat the same foods served. Over time, they started to enjoy this process. It pays to set a standard and stick to it. Believe me, you will have them eating whatever you put in front of them in no time. Don't forget children like to be appreciated for their achievements.

When I got my boys involved in the kitchen, I wanted to make sure they understood how to use the tools and how to feed themselves and others, but most importantly, how to keep themselves safe in a minefield of hot pots and pans, knives, and stove top surfaces. What works is giving them a choice of what they want to do in the kitchen, whether cleaning and slicing vegetables, preparing the salad, or formulating homemade salad dressing. Involving them in the menu planning, the grocery shopping, the preparation, and ultimately the cooking, will pay off ten times over when they are begging you to let them help you.

Don't be too strict in the kitchen. Let them make a bit of a mess as long as they learn to clean it up! You want them to think of it as a friendly, welcoming place. When I plan our weekly menus, I get both of my son's input when making the shopping list. Of course, that isn't always realistic, but I always ask on a regular basis if there is something they would like to eat. Below are some tips when involving your kids in the entire process.

Menu Planning:

This is the perfect training ground for a solid food foundation. "Is there something special you would like to try this week?" "Sure mom, I want to have chicken tenders." This opens the door to what to include along side that food choice for a balanced meal, "Which vegetable do you prefer to pair with this: zucchini or carrots?"

Shopping:

Navigating the grocery store helps to familiarize them with lay of the land. This is the perfect place to discuss healthy snack choices and teach them what to look for in a label and what to avoid in the ingredient list.

Gardening:

Having small potted herbs on the windowsill, or a garden full of fresh herbs and vegetables teaches kids the responsibility that goes into growing food and makes them appreciate what they're eating.

Preparation:

It seems like a daunting task to involve your kids in the kitchen, with thoughts of flour fights and bowls turned upside down and who gets to lick the spoon! Patience and perseverance will have its rewards...just take a deep breath and learn to enjoy the process.

Know Your Child:

Your children are going to have different levels of interest so don't get frustrated, but turn that into a plus when delegating what task each should perform. One may be better at handling the stove and the other at mixing.

Know Your Comfort Zone:

This one is very important because ultimately you are in the driver's seat. There are certain tasks that stress you out in the kitchen; consider doing those on your own like working out a complicated recipe. They are better left with you in peace.

Make It Interesting:

We know children have an attention span that lasts maybe five minutes (if we are lucky). I recommend inviting the little helpers into the kitchen on the weekends when you're not as stressed out by the weekly duties. You want to enjoy this family time as much as they do. Make sure you choose fun and whimsical recipes that the kids will enjoy and start out by creating tasks like cracking the eggs into the bowl. Get them engaged in the food dialogue, the recipe ingredients, the spices, and the baking time.

Kids Are Not Going To Like Every Kind Of Food:

I'm not going to change around a whole meal plan if someone doesn't like a side dish. I will substitute it with a green vegetable they do like. We still sit down as a family and eat the same meal with a few exceptions. Kitchen family time is part of the early building blocks to establishing a healthy relationship with food. Keep in mind that each child is different, and learning kitchen skills can differ with their level of maturity. The recommendations below are adapted from guidelines for cooking with young children from "The National Network for Child Care."

The average 2-year-old can do the following:
- scrubbing fruits and vegetables
- wiping the countertops and table
- dipping one ingredient into another
- tearing lettuce and spinach leaves in bite-size pieces
- crushing crackers or corn chips into crumbs for breading
- sprinkling cheese
- snapping fresh green beans
- arranging foods on a baking pan

The average 3-year-old can do all of the above, plus:
- pouring measured liquids into a bowl of dry ingredients
- mixing batter; stirring or whisking ingredients together
- shaking a jar of homemade salad dressing
- spread nut butter on firm bread
- cutting soft foods, such as bananas, with a plastic serrated knife

Safety First:

- Make sure that each child has a space to work. It should be away from hot stoves and pans, as well as knives and other sharp objects.
- Never leave a child unsupervised in the kitchen. Make sure kids understand safety rules and that they know only a grown-up should use the stove, electric equipment or sharp knives.
- Make sure all the helpers wash their hands before preparing. Start with a clean kitchen and always keep counters free of clutter.
- Wash all fruits and vegetables thoroughly.
- Work slowly and carefully on one thing at a time. Having kids help in the kitchen will slow you down, but you're creating a lifetime of memories that are worth it!
- Do not put pots and pans on a high shelf. As a kid, I chipped my front tooth when a pot fell on my face!

"Do Not Give In To Pressure From Anyone"

Ruth J. Katz

My sons Jonah and Jordan

12

Other Parents and Caregivers and Their Tips

―――――――

When I started formulating this book, I reached out to other parents I knew in order to learn what tips worked for feeding their families healthy. I love sharing what I have learned with others, and my friends are happy to share back. Taking care of my family and myself has always been a major priority to me and it shows in how good I feel! I am honored to know I've helped to inspire others along the way. Despite my knowledge in health and nutrition, there is always more to learn. There are so many books, blogs, and websites that offer many different opinions on health and wellness. I take it all in and find what works for me.

Studying at the Institute for Integrated Nutrition gave me the opportunity to meet so many like-minded people on the same type of wellness journey. I remember my mom asking me about my first day of class at Lincoln Center in 2009. My response was that "It was like being in a room with 1600 other individuals like myself that were on the same mission and had the same passion and philosophies on nutrition." It felt like home as many shared my proactive views on health. I was surrounded by productive people that wanted to make positive changes for the world. Many of the graduates have since created wellness businesses, published books, and started health organizations. I asked friends to contribute their ideas to this book in hopes that it will inspire you to nourish your family and maintain a healthy lifestyle while thriving in your career, and life!

Laura M. – *mother of three, health coach, fitness & lifestyle blogger, ACE personal trainer*

I introduced my children to healthy food when they could barely walk! When my kids would sit down for a little TV time, I would bring them a plate of raw carrots and a bowl of hummus on the side. Now, if I had brought them a plate of cookies or a bowl of chips, they probably would have mindlessly chowed down on those. Introducing healthy eating at an early age is vital. As a working mother, it can be a challenge to get a healthy meal on the table and make sure we fit in quality exercise and activities. Prepping meals for the week is a timesaver. Life is already so hectic, so a little prep time can make all the difference between healthy food choices or being at the mercy of quick yet unhealthy food. The most important part of our day is when we can sit down as a family and have dinner together. We talk about our day, school, friends, upcoming events, even politics. I relish these dinners together and encourage my friends to prioritize family dinner time. I believe this is a cornerstone of a solid, trusting relationship with our children and I hope they will carry this tradition forward when they are parents.

Darren P. – *attorney*

I have them involved in gardening and cooking. They pick the tomatoes and the basil and make salad. It works because if they pick them, they should eat them, and the ripe heirloom tomatoes taste great.

Roberta F. – *mother of one, pharmaceutical sales*

I steam a lot of veggies like broccoli, and carrots and I leave them in the fridge for snacking!

Ellen M. – *mother of three*

If your children see you eat healthy, they will follow suit. I keep the bad stuff out of the house. I always leave fruit out on the kitchen table.

Julie T. – *mother of one, retail loan originator*

I sprinkle flax seeds over my son's breakfast and dinner foods without him knowing. One day when I was making pancakes, he came in and asked if he could try the flax seeds. After he ate them, he thought that it was not bad. That's when I told he had been eating them for years.

Robyn K. – *mother of two, real estate specialist*

I don't keep juice, soda, or any sugary drinks in my house. My kids drink filtered water, and on occasion homemade lemonade.

Sari R. – *mother of two, senior lending officer*

We avoid soda as phosphorus can inhibit calcium absorption for growing children. It also has a lot of high-fructose corn syrup.

Jacky T. – *mother of two, real estate broker*

When my sons were babies, we cooked them solid foods and exposed them to different tastes. When they got older they still ate dinner with us. They ate what we ate for dinner, which was real food. When we took them to restaurants, instead of ordering from the kids menu, they had real food from the regular menu.

Bonnie L. – *mother of two*

We always enjoy making our own pizza with high-quality ingredients such as gluten-free dough. They love making their own decisions about toppings. The taste and quality far surpassed any pizza joints. They quickly learned homemade is the way to go. We did the same with guacamole and tacos. They use turkey or bison with all organic and assorted toppings.

Andrea W. – *grandmother of 4, luxury real estate agent*

My tips are: Make kale chips for a snack, serve celery with almond butter or sunflower butter (if nut allergy) and make fruit kabobs. Kids love them.

Susan M. – *mother of two, title company owner*

Have them help you prepare the meal. I've had my older son help me in the kitchen since he was three and it made him more aware of what we were eating and why. The gluten-free and dye-free diet has also been key.

Michelle B. – *mother of three, real estate investor*

If they are never exposed to fast food, they won't know to ask for it. Set good examples by having the adults eat their veggies. Prepare meals with good flavors. For example, when I make pasta sauce, I have them pick out the onions, mushrooms and peppers and try a bite size before adding in the recipe. Early on introduce them to fish, veggies, and unusual fruit. Make fruit kabobs and cut fruit and leave it on the counter for when they come home from school to snack, they will eat it if it's out. Teach them to read the labels for serving sizes (especially for chips) and which ingredients are good or bad.

Carolyn K. – *mother of two, entrepreneur*

Make colorful plates with veggies. Garden if possible so they can watch food grow. Let the kids help you create simple recipes. Meals should be a special time for gathering and sharing. Happy healthy food makes for smiling faces.

"Yesterday Is Gone.
Tomorrow Has Not Yet Come.
We Have Only Today. Let Us Begin."

Mother Teresa

13

I Hungry For Breakfast, Lunch, Dinner, Snacks, and Dessert

When I traced the meaning of breakfast, I found that it comes from the idea that it's been several hours since dinner, so in the morning you eat to "break your fast"...and my boys are always ready to rise and shine with a hearty breakfast! Lunch is an abbreviation taken from the more formal word "Lunchentach," from 1850, meaning a meal that was inserted between more substantial meals. This was an extra meal between midday dinner and supper, especially during the long hours of hard labor in harvesting season. This applies in modern times to our little ones as they soldier on throughout their school day with a nutritious lunch, which is vital for cognitive function.

By the 1730s, the upper class was waking up later and dining at 3 or 4 pm and by 1770, their dinner was at 4 or 5 pm. A formal evening meal lit by candles (sometimes accompanied with entertainment) was a "Supper Party." The French have always considered this the main meal of the day. The total sum of the day is always wrapped around our family dinner and remains something to which we all look forward.

Below is a list of healthy options that fall into each meal time.

I Hungry...for breakfast
- Baked eggs in a bell pepper or on a half of avocado
- Flax bread with egg and smoked salmon
- Homemade paleo bread with turkey, eggs or smoked salmon
- Yogurt made from coconut milk with fresh fruit
- Eggs with black beans, avocado, diced tomatoes
- Fruit salads with raw honey, crushed nuts, shaved coconut
- Oatmeal with coconut milk, flax and chia seeds
- Chia seeds in coconut milk with bananas
- Nut butters with strawberries or bananas, rice cakes, or flax crackers

- Paleo eggs and veggie muffins
- Smoothie of bananas, coconut milk with coconut flakes and cinnamon
- Rolled up turkey over carrots
- Paleo pumpkin puree pancakes
- Sliced bananas and raspberries in coconut milk with cinnamon & chia
- Baked egg pizza on rice tortilla with tomatoes, sausage links
- Applegate farms sausages or bacon
- Sardines in tomato sauce on flexseed crackers

I Hungry..for lunch

- Sliced chicken in lettuce/rice tortilla with tahini, shredded carrots & raisins
- Cucumber and avocado rolls with rice
- Wild salmon over greens (arugula, watercress)
- Egg salad with paleo bread
- Chickpeas with curry, honey, raisins, sliced almonds, shredded coconut
- Sliced turkey with lettuce, tomato and cheese, in rice tortilla
- Guacamole, chicken, shredded carrots, tomatoes, lettuce or rice tortilla
- Avocado and vegetable cucumber sandwich
- Baked sweet potato with tuna salad
- Avocado, sprouts, and vegan cheese on paleo bread
- Eggplant-wrapped melon
- Taco salad of meat or beans, pico de gallo, rice, and lettuce
- Paleo bread, avocado, tomato, salt, black sesame seeds, olive oil
- Falafel balls with tahini

I Hungry...for dinner

- Salmon or flounder with mango sticky rice and greens
- Skewers (chicken, beef, lamb) or kabobs
- Vegetable stir-fry
- Vegetable sushi rolls
- Chicken tenders with paleo coconut bread crumbs
- Chicken with rice noodles
- Bean or chicken, avocado pico de gallo burrito
- Chicken wings in Bone Sucking Sauce
- Turkey chili
- Baked butternut squash with chicken, tuna, egg salad or vegetables with melted cheese

- Wild salmon with raw honey
- Quinoa with raisins and chickpeas
- Spaghetti squash baked with tomato sauce, ground beef or ground turkey
- Grilled zucchini with melted cheese
- Gluten-free pasta with olive oil, shrimp, and veggies
- Lentil soup
- Zucchini lasagna
- Grilled shrimp with melon and pineapple salsa
- Baked sweet potatoes sliced & drizzled with olive oil

I Hungry...for a snack

- Fruit and nut bars
- Crudités with hummus
- Guacamole with corn chips or cut carrots and celery
- Pickles
- Air-popped popcorn with olive oil and sea salt
- Homemade pops (chocolate milk, pomegranate juice, coconut milks)
- Homemade fruit rollups
- Sliced apples or pears with nut butter or tahini
- Kale chips
- Toasted chickpeas
- Plantain chips
- Baked yam chips with hummus
- Edamame
- Hard-boiled eggs
- Homemade granola
- Sulfite-free dried fruits
- Nori sheets
- Almond butter on celery stalk with sesame seeds
- Guacamole with jicama sticks
- Honey sesame treats
- Flax crackers with vegan cheese or avocado
- Warm almond milk with cinnamon

I Hungry...for dessert

- Macaroons
- Fruit kebabs, Grilled fruit
- Homemade applesauce

- Rice pudding or chia pudding made with coconut milk
- Lychee nuts in almond milk
- Balls made from nut butter, coconut, and honey
- Melon, avocado, and figs
- Coconut ice cream with fresh fruit and coconut flakes
- Frozen bananas dipped in dark chocolate

"Rotate Your Foods"

Ruth J. Katz

14

Fourteen Days of Quick Easy Meals

I have put together a fourteen-day plan below that will put you and your family on track and give you ideas on what to eat. Cooking and preparing meals at home will benefit your health and your wallet! At home you have the ability to control your ingredients and source the highest quality foods. I realize that most of us don't have the time to cook three meals a day, seven days a week. We often times have had a hectic day, with barely enough time to put our feet on the ground after getting the kids fed. I recommend you kick start this plan on a Saturday when your are less stressed and can involve your kids in the planning, buying, preparing, and sitting down and sharing it as a family meal.

I have listed out the recipes but you can also buy these foods prepared store bought if needed. I live in Manhattan and sometimes order takeout and buy prepared foods. Do what works for you. Please understand that this menu is free of dairy and gluten as that is how I eat. Feel free to make substitutions as you see fit. Happy Cooking!

The full recipes are in part 3.

Day 1
Breakfast: Paleo everything bagel & pineapple ginger smoothie
Lunch: Taco salad with beef, beans, and avocado slices
Dinner: Zucchini lasagna
Dessert: Coconut macaroons

Day 2
Breakfast: Baked egg in avocado
Lunch: Lentil soup with spinach & Chicken salad with mango
Dinner: Fish tacos & Avocado arugula salad
Dessert: Frozen fruit cup made with Yonana machine

Day 3

Breakfast: Baked oatmeal overnight
Lunch: Baked butternut squash stuffed with tuna salad
Dinner: Turkey chili & Avocado hummus with flaxseed crackers
Dessert: Baked apples

Day 4

Breakfast: Rice cake face with nut butter & Ambrosia parfait
Lunch: Smoky eggplant and melon wraps & Black bean soup with avocado
Dinner: Spaghetti squash bolognese & Grilled asparagus and prosciutto
Dessert: Homemade fruit roll-up

Day 5

Breakfast: Paleo waffles
Lunch: Creamy chicken salad stuffed avocado
Dinner: Salmon veggie kabob
Dessert: Chocolate avocado mousse

Day 6

Breakfast: Turkey and egg frittata
Lunch: Greek salad with shrimp or chicken
Dinner: Honey macadamia halibut & Baked carrot "fries"
Dessert: Key lime coconut popsicles

Day 7

Breakfast: Fruit salad with coconut yogurt
Lunch: Turkey cutlets & Raw carrot salad
Dinner: Paleo lasagna
Dessert: Healthy crunch bars

Day 8

Breakfast: Chia pudding
Lunch: Tahini chicken wraps
Dinner: Coconut curry fish
Dessert: Salted dark chocolate nut and fruit clusters

Day 9

Breakfast: Veggie frittata
Lunch: Grilled pepper steak salad
Dinner: Gluten-free fish sticks & Green salad
Dessert: Grilled mango and peaches with honey

Day 10

Breakfast: Smoked salmon on paleo bread & Coconut blueberry smoothie
Lunch: Turkey burger with lettuce wraps
Dinner: Lamb kabobs with veggies & Roasted broccoli & cauliflower
Dessert: Lychee coconut and lime popsicles

Day 11

Breakfast: Hard-boiled pasture-raised eggs & Raw carrots and apple slices
Lunch: Sautéed organic chicken tenders with peanut sauce
Dinner: Grilled shrimp with mango salsa
Dessert: Frozen bananas in dark chocolate

Day 12

Breakfast: Gluten-free blueberry pancakes with fresh pomegranate walnut paste
Lunch: Grass-fed burger with Sweet potato fries
Dinner: Cod cakes with salad
Dessert: Gluten-free cake pops

Day 13

Breakfast: Tomato egg dish & Bacon-wrapped figs
Lunch: Avocado cucumber and turkey sandwich
Dinner: Maple chili glazed pork medallions & Baked zucchini chips
Dessert: Banana and Chocolate pudding

Day 14

Breakfast: BLT egglets
Lunch: Bento box lunch
Dinner: Shrimp avocado salad
Dessert: Watermelon Pizza

PART III

Recipes, Resources, Useful Tips

Health Care Begins In Your Lifestyle And Kitchen

14-Day Meal Plan

Day 1 Breakfast: Paleo Everything Bagels

(Recipe by Rachel Mansfield)

Ingredients (Makes 6–7 bagels)
- 4 pasture-raised eggs
- 3 tablespoons of avocado oil
- 1 tablespoon of unpasteurized apple
- Cider vinegar 2 tablespoons of water or bone broth
- 1¼ cup almond flour or almond
- Meal ¼ cup tapioca flour or arrowroot flour
- 3 tablespoons of coconut flour
- 1 teaspoon of baking powder

Trader Joe's Everything But the Bagel Seasoning to sprinkle

Directions:
- Preheat oven to 350 degrees and grease a donut pan with avocado oil.
- Whisk together eggs, oil, apple cider vinegar, and water or bone broth together until fully combined.
- Mix in the almond flour, coconut flour, tapioca flour, and baking powder and mix until smooth and there are no clumps in the batter.
- Fill each donut mold with batter; then sprinkle everything but the bagel seasoning on top.
- Bake in oven for 10–12 minutes (or until ready – I stick a toothpick in).
- Allow the bagels to cool for a few minutes; then remove from pan.
- Add dairy-free butter or dairy-free cream cheese of choice on top.

Pineapple Ginger Smoothie

Ingredients: Serves 2

- 2-3 cups of organic frozen pineapple
- 1-2 cups of organic coconut milk (If you want thicker, then add less liquid)
- 2 cups of ice cubes
- 2 1-inch pieces of fresh ginger
- For protein: 2 scoops of collagen protein powder
- Option to add honey but the ginger and pineapple combination is pretty sweet

Directions:

- Blend pineapple, ginger, milk, and ice.
- Pour into glasses and sprinkle nutmeg or cinnamon.

Day 1 Lunch: Taco Salad With Beef, Beans, and Avocado Slices

Ingredients: Serves 4

- Half a cup of prepared salsa or pico de gallo
- 1 teaspoon of macadamia nut oil
- 1 medium organic onion chopped
- 3 cloves of minced organic garlic
- 1 pound of ground lean organic grass-fed beef
- 2 large plum organic tomatoes diced
- 1 (14 ounce) can of organic kidney beans

- 2 teaspoons of ground cumin
- 2 teaspoons of chili powder
- ¼ chopped fresh cilantro
- 2 heads of shredded organic lettuce
- 1 organic avocado
- 1 organic lime

Directions:

- Heat oil in a large skillet over medium heat.
- Add onion and garlic and cook, stirring often until softened about two minutes.
- Add beef and cook, stirring often and crumbling with a wooden spoon until cooked through about five minutes.
- Add tomatoes, beans, cumin, and chili powder.
- Cook stirring until the tomatoes begin to break down 2–3 minutes. Remove from the heat, and stir in cilantro and salsa/pico de gallo. To serve, divide the lettuce among four plates.
- Top lettuce with meat mixture and salsa or pico de gallo and a lime wedge with cut avocado slices.

Day 1 Dinner: Zucchini Lasagna
(made with zucchini instead of pasta)

Ingredients: Serves 6–8

- 6 large organic zucchinis (skin off and sliced lengthwise in thin strips– as thin as possible)
- 1 cup of sliced mushrooms 2 bell peppers sliced
- 1 onion chopped
- 2 cloves of minced garlic
- 2 cups of sliced/chopped broccoli 6 cups of chopped spinach
- 1 large can of organic roma basil tomatoes, 1 cup of dairy-free chunky ricotta cheese
- 1 cup of organic coconut yogurt
- 1 cup of shredded dairy-free mozzarella cheese; dried herbs to taste: oregano, basil, thyme; salt to taste

Directions:

- Sautée all veggies in a pan in coconut oil.
- Add in garlic, onions towards the end and season with Italian herbs: oregano, basil, thyme, salt and pepper to taste.
- Mix yogurt and cheese well and and add some salt to taste.
- Grease a 6 × 8" glass baking pan with olive oil and layer the zucchini slices as the 1st layer. Next layer: sautéed veggies, then cheese and yogurt, then tomatoes, and repeat until about ½ inch left at the top of the baking pan or you run out of food.
- Top layer: spread the yogurt and cheese.
- Top with fresh basil leaves if you want.
- Bake for 45 minutes at 400 degrees.
- Prepare a salad while waiting if you please.
- Allow to cool for 5 minutes before serving.

Day 1 Dessert: Coconut Macaroons

(Recipe influenced by All recipes)

Ingredients: Yields 15

- 2 pasture-raised eggs
- 3 tablespoons of organic coconut milk
- 2 tablespoons of organic maple syrup or raw honey
- 2 teaspoons of organic coconut sugar
- 1 pinch Himalayan or sea salt
- 1.5 teaspoons of organic vanilla extract
- 1 cup of organic shredded coconut

Directions:

- Preheat oven to 350 degrees. Line 2 baking sheets with parchment paper.
- Mix eggs, sweetener in a bowl until creamy, about 2 minutes. Add coconut milk, vanilla and salt and mix well; mix in coconut until a dense, sticky batter forms.
- Take 1 tbsp of batter and roll into a sphere. Place on the baking sheet and repeat with remaining batter.
- Bake in oven for 10 minutes. Then, flip macaroons and bake until lightly golden, about 5 minutes more.
- Allow to cool on baking sheet for 1 minute and then transfer to wire rack to cool completely.

Day 2 Breakfast: Baked Egg in Avocado

Ingredients: Serves 4

- 2 ripe organic avocados
- 4 fresh pasture-raised eggs
- 1 tablespoon of chopped nitrate-free bacon (already cooked)
- Salt and pepper to taste
- (Serve with paleo everything bagels if you want)

Directions:

- Preheat the oven to 425 degrees.
- Slice the avocados in half and take out the pit.
- Scoop out about two tablespoons of flesh from the center of the avocado so the egg will fit in.
- Place the avocados in a small baking dish.
- Crack an egg into each avocado half.
- Crack the yolk in first, and then let the egg whites spill in to fill up the rest of the shell.
- Place in the oven and bake for 15 to 20 minutes.
- Cooking time will depend on the size of your eggs and avocados.
- Make sure the egg whites have enough time to set.
- Remove from oven and season with salt, pepper, bacon, parsley, cilantro, etc.

Day 2 Lunch: Lentil Soup with Spinach

Ingredients: Serves 4

- 1 teaspoon of organic olive oil
- 1 organic onion diced, 1 organic carrot sliced
- 4 cups of vegetable or chicken broth
- 1 cup of dry lentils (pre-soak them to reduce lectin content)
- ¼ tsp of pepper, ¼ tsp of dried thyme, 2 bay leaves
- Dash 1 tbsp of Himalayan-salted lemon juice
- 1 bag of baby organic spinach

Directions:

- In a large pot, sauté the onions and carrot in the oil for 3–5 minutes until onions turn clear.
- Add the vegetable broth, lentils, pepper, thyme, bay leaves, and salt.
- Reduce heat to a simmer.
- Cover and cook the lentils for about 45 minutes until they are soft.
- Remove bay leaves and stir in the spinach and lemon juice before serving.

Day 2 Lunch: Chicken Salad with Mango

Ingredients: Serves 4

- ¼ cup of mayonnaise no soybean oil (Brand: Primal Kitchen) 1 tsp of curry powder
- 2 cups of cubed cooked organic pasture-raised chicken, 1 peeled and diced organic mango
- ¼ diced organic celery stalk
- ¼ cup of toasted organic almond slices

Directions:

- Mix mayonnaise and curry powder in a large bowl.
- Toss in chicken, peeled and diced mango, celery stalk, and almond slices.

Day 2 Dinner: Fish Tacos

Ingredients: Yields 12 tacos

- 1 pound of boneless and skinless wild tilapia or white fish fillets (make sure not frozen from China)
- Organic olive oil
- Himalayan salt or sea salt to taste Pepper to taste
- ¾ cup and 2 tablespoons of fresh salsa or pico de gallo 12 organic corn tortillas
- Shredded organic lettuce, 2 sliced organic avocados

Directions:

- Cut fish into 2-inch pieces and rinse and pat dry; Heat broiler, with rack in highest position.
- Place fish on rimmed baking sheet and drizzle with olive oil Season with salt and pepper.
- Broil until fish is lightly browned on top, 5–10 minutes, until flesh is opaque throughout.
- Warm the tortillas on a pan.
- Divide fish evenly among tortillas and top with fresh salsa and avocado.

Day 2 Dinner: Avocado Arugula Salad

Ingredients: Serves 4–6

- 6 cups of organic arugula leaves
- 1 avocado peeled and sliced
- ½ red onion sliced rinsed and drained, 1 tbsp of lime juicer

For Orange Vinaigrette:

- 1 tbsp of champagne vinegar (or apple cider vinegar)
- 4 tbsp of orange juice (½ an orange)
- 2 tbsp of lime juice (½ lime) ½ tsp of cumin
- 2 tbsp of finely chopped cilantro, 1 red chili or hot pepper sliced, salt and pepper to taste

Directions:
- Combine all ingredients for salad dressing in a tightly closed jar and shake well until mixed.
- Toss the arugula leaves with half of the vinaigrette.
- Add avocado slices and onion slices to the arugula mix. Drizzle remaining dressing on top.

Day 2 Dessert: Frozen Fruit Custard Made with Yonana Machine

Ingredients: Serves 4
- 4 peeled frozen organic bananas
- 1 package each of frozen organic peaches, blueberries, strawberries optional toppings: Semi-sweet cacao nibs, mint leaves, cinnamon, shredded coconut, dates, raw honey

Directions:
- Put frozen bananas through the Yonana machine to turn it to a custard form.
- Add some frozen fruit from each package through the Yonana machine.
- Top with shredded coconut as sprinkles and semi-sweet cacao nibs.

Day 3 Breakfast: Baked Oatmeal Overnight

(This recipe requires prep the night before serving)

Ingredients: Serves 4–6

- 2 large pasture-raised eggs, room temperature, lightly beaten 3 cups of organic coconut milk
- ¾ cup of coconut sugar, maple syrup or honey
- Pinch of Himalayan salt
- 1½ tsp of cinnamon ¼ cup of coconut oil
- Optional toppings: crushed organic walnuts, fresh organic berries, sliced almonds, dried fruit

Directions:

- In a large bowl, whisk together eggs, milk, sugar, oil, cinnamon, salt.
- Stir in oats and dried fruit.
- Pour into a greased 8 × 8 baking dish. Cover and refrigerate overnight.
- Next morning, preheat oven to 350 F. Remove dish from refrigerator and stir oatmeal.
- Bake uncovered until golden brown (40–50 minutes).
- Add toppings as you please.

Day 3 Lunch: Baked Butternut Squash Stuffed with Tuna Salad

Ingredients: Serves 4

- 2 organic butternut squash
- 1 tablespoon of macadamia or coconut oil, Himalayan Salt and pepper to taste
- 1 can of wild tuna packed in water
- 1 tablespoon of avocado mayonnaise (brand: Primal Kitchen made of avocado oil)
- Choice of seasoning for tuna: dill, oregano, thyme, paprika—your call!
- Dairy-free cheese for sprinkling

Directions:

- Preheat oven to 350° degrees.
- Cut squash in half lengthwise and remove seeds. Coat squash lightly with oil, salt, and pepper.
- Bake in the preheated oven until tender and easily pierced with a fork.
- Scoop out middle of squash and add tuna salad made with wild canned tuna packed in water mixed with mayonnaise.

- Melt cheese on top.
- Other options for filing can be chicken salad, egg salad, or grilled vegetables.

Day 3 Dinner: Turkey Chili

Ingredients: Serves 4

- 2 teaspoons plus 1 tablespoon macadamia nut oil
- 1 pound of 93% lean ground organic turkey, 2 medium organic onions chopped
- 4 cloves of minced organic garlic, 2 tablespoons of chili powder
- 1 tablespoon of ground cumin
- ½ teaspoon of ground cinnamon ¼ teaspoon of Himalayan salt
- 2 cups of filtered water
- 8 ripe crushed organic tomatoes
- 1 15-ounce can of organic small red beans, kidney or pinto beans, rinsed
- ¼ cup of sliced organic green olives rinsed

Directions:

- Heat 2 tablespoons of oil over medium heat. Add turkey and cook.
- Stir and break up with wooden spoon until no longer pink, 3 to 4 minutes.
- Transfer to a plate.
- Reduce heat to medium and add the remaining 1 tablespoon of oil to the pan.

- Add onions and garlic and cook stirring often until beginning to soften and brown slightly 5 to 7 minutes.
- Stir in chili powder, cumin, cinnamon, pepper, and salt. Add water, tomatoes, beans, olives, and turkey.
- Bring to a boil over medium high heat.
- Reduce heat to maintain a simmer and cook until the vegetables are soft for 10 to 15 minutes.

Creamy Avocado Hummus with Flaxseed Crackers
makes about 3 cups

Ingredients:

- 1 15-ounce can of organic chickpeas, drained and presoaked
- 2 ripe organic avocados cut into chunks, ½ cup of organic olive oil
- ¼ cup of fresh lemon juice
- 1½ tablespoons of organic tahini 1 clove garlic
- Himalayan salt and pepper to taste
- For dipping: Organic green bell pepper sliced, organic sliced cucumber, organic celery or organic carrots.

- Organic flaxseed crackers for serving

Directions:

- For an extra smooth hummus spread, take the time to remove the skins from the chickpeas.
- In the bowl of a food processor, combine chickpeas. Add a good pinch of salt and pepper.
- Blend until combined and smooth for about 3 minutes. Add more salt and pepper and lemon if necessary. Blend for another 5 minutes until light and smooth. Top with a bit of olive oil, salt, and pepper.
- Serve with fresh vegetables and flax cracker chips.

Day 3 Dessert: Baked Apples

(This dish has the best aroma)

Ingredients: Serves 4

- 4 organic apples
- Cinnamon
- Organic raw honey
- Organic walnuts

Directions:

- Cut apples with an apple slicer and put on a baking sheet covered with foil.
- Sprinkle them with cinnamon and raw honey.
- In a food processor crush walnuts until finely grounded. Add walnuts or nut of choice.
- Bake until soft and golden.

Day 4 Breakfast: Rice Cake Face with Nut Butter

Ingredients: Serves 1
- Organic rice cakes
- Organic nut butter of almond
- Organic blueberries or kiwi
- Organic strawberries, organic banana

Directions:
- Take a brown rice cake from Lundberg and spread nut butter made from almonds.
- Add blueberries or kiwis for eyes, a strawberry for the nose, and a banana for the smile.

Day 4 Breakfast: Ambrosia Parfait

(You can assemble this the night before and store in the refrigerator)

Ingredients: Serves 4
- 2 cups of organic coconut yogurt, ½ cup of organic blueberries, ½ cup of organic strawberries
- 2 tablespoons of sliced organic almonds toasted
- 2 tablespoons of toasted shredded organic coconut

Directions:

- Mix the fruit together and set aside.
- Mix the coconut and almonds and set aside. Place ⅓ of yogurt into 4 parfait glasses.
- Layer ⅓ of the fruit mixture on top of the yogurt. Sprinkle ⅓ of the almonds and coconut on top. Repeat the process again for 3 layers.

Day 4 Lunch: Smoky Eggplant and Melon Wraps

Ingredients: Makes 24 wraps

- 1 medium organic eggplant
- ¼ cup of organic olive oil
- 2 tablespoons of coconut aminos (instead of soy sauce), 2 tablespoons of organic apple cider vinegar
- 2 teaspoons of smoked paprika, 1½ teaspoon of cumin
- 2 teaspoons of Himalayan salt, 2 pound organic cantaloupe

Directions:

- Peel and cut cantaloupe into 24 1-inch chunks.
- Quarter eggplant lengthwise and slice into 24 long, very thin strips using sharp vegetable peeler.

- Whisk together oil, coconut aminos, vinegar, paprika, cumin, and salt in a 9-inch square baking dish.
- Add eggplant strips and let them marinate for 10 minutes. Heat gas grill to high.
- Grill eggplant strips for 2 minutes per side until they are very tender with pronounced grill marks.
- Wrap 1 strip grilled eggplant around each melon chunk, and secure with a toothpick.

Day 4 Lunch: Black Bean Soup with Avocado

Ingredients: Serves 8

- 2 tablespoons of organic olive oil
- 1 red onion, small diced
- 4 to 6 cloves of minced organic garlic
- 1 heaping tablespoon of whole cumin seeds, crushed or left whole 1 tablespoon chipotle chile powder
- 1 to 2 cinnamon sticks
- 2 teaspoons of Himalayan salt, 2 tablespoons of raw honey
- 1 small to medium bunch organic cilantro, coarsely chopped
- 4 to 6 medium organic tomatoes, seeded and coarsely chopped
- 3 cans of organic black beans, 4 cups of drained vegetable stock
- 1 to 2 organic avocados cubed, juice from 1 fresh lime

Directions:

- In a soup pot, sauté onion until soft, for 5 to 7 minutes.
- Add garlic, cumin, chipotle powder, cinnamon, salt, honey and half of the cilantro. Sauté for an additional 2 to 3 minutes, stirring often.
- Add tomatoes and beans.
- Sauté for an additional 2–3 minutes.
- Add stock and bring to a boil.
- Simmer for 10 to 15 minutes.
- Blend a cup or two of beans and liquid and return back to pot. Stir in avocado, lime juice, and remaining cilantro.
- Season with salt.

Day 4 Dinner: Spaghetti Squash Bolognese

Ingredients: Serves 4
- 1-2 Medium spaghetti squash
- 2 Cans of organic whole peeled tomatoes—mashed up, 2 tbsp of avocado oil
- 1-2 tbsp of Italian herbs (basil, oregano, thyme, rosemary), 2 cloves of diced garlic
- 1/3 Large onion dinner diced, 1 medium grated carrot
- 1 tbsp of vegan parmesan cheese
- 1-2 pounds of grass-fed ground beef (or turkey, bison, lamb) seasoned with salt, pepper, garlic powder, oregano, thyme, basil)

Directions:
- Heat oven to 400 degrees F.
- Cut spaghetti squash in half lengthwise, scoop out seeds and brush interior with some oil.
- Place each half on a baking dish cut-side down.
- While the squash is in oven, in a large saucepan, over medium heat, place oil, onion and garlic. Cook until soft (about 8-10 minutes).
- Add in carrots, salt and pepper and cook for another 3-5 minutes. Add mashed-up tomatoes to the saucepan.

- Stir in herbs and add more salt and pepper to taste. Allow the sauce to simmer for 20-30 minutes.
- In a separate pan, on medium heat, pour some olive oil and heat up the turkey until no longer pink (probably 5 minutes). Once the sauce is done with simmering, place spinach and ground meat in pan. Spinach should cook quickly.
- Add sauce with beef/turkey to spaghetti squash. Sprinkle some grated cheese!

Day 4 Dinner: Grilled Asparagus with Prosciutto

Ingredients: Serves 4

- 1 pound of organic asparagus spears trimmed
- Nitrate-free organic prosciutto, 1 tbsp of avocado oil
- Himalayan or sea salt and pepper to taste

Directions:

- Preheat grill for high heat.
- Lightly coat the asparagus spears with olive oil.
- Wrap asparagus with prosciutto; season with salt and pepper to taste.
- Grill over high heat for 2–3 minutes.

Day 4 Dessert: Homemade Fruit Roll-up

Ingredients:

- 4 cups of mixed frozen berries (e.g., raspberries, blueberries, strawberries, and blackberries)
- ½ cup of unsweetened applesauce
- 1 teaspoon of lemon juice
- ¼ teaspoon of lemon zest
- 1 tablespoon of honey or as desired sweetness (you may need more if your berries are really sour)

Directions:

- Mix all of the ingredients in a saucepan over medium-high heat. Simmer for 20 minutes, until the berries have popped and some of the liquid has evaporated.
- Blend mixture in blender until smooth.
- Pour half of mixture on 1 parchment paper lined baking sheet and the other half on another parchment paper-lined baking sheet.
- Spread mixture with a spatula evenly across the baking sheet, to about ⅛ inch thick.

- If you have a dehydrator with a fan in the back, these will only take about 3 hours on the high (150 degrees) setting. Without a fan, they'll take about 8-10 hours on 150 degrees.
- You will know they're done when you touch them lightly with your finger and they are no longer sticky. If the edges get a little too brittle and dry, you can brush a tiny bit of water over it and will be good as new!

Day 5 Breakfast: Paleo Waffles

Ingredients: Serves 4–6

- 3 large pasture-raised eggs
- ¾ cup of whole macadamia nuts
- ¼ cup of raw pecans
- ¼ cup of coconut milk
- 3 tablespoons of coconut oil, melted
  2 tablespoons of raw honey
- ¼ cup of organic coconut flour
- ¾ teaspoon of baking soda
- ¼ teaspoon of sea salt
- 2 teaspoons of pumpkin pie spice

Directions:

- Blend the eggs, macadamia nuts, pecans, milk, honey, and melted coconut oil in a blender until creamy.
- Add the salt, baking soda, coconut flour, and spice and blend again for about 30 seconds until fully incorporated.
- Pour the batter into the preheated waffle maker (if oil is needed, use some coconut oil).
- Cook the waffles until the waffle iron has stopped steaming, about 45 seconds. Each waffle iron may differ in cook times. Repeat until the batter has been used up.
- Serve hot with maple syrup, berries, fruit, bacon, etc.

Day 5 Lunch: Creamy Chicken Salad Stuffed Avocado

Ingredients: Serves 4

- 1 tablespoon of tahini (or nut-butter of choice)
- 1 tablespoon of brown rice vinegar
- Juice from 1 lime, plus zest from half of lime, 2 cloves of chopped garlic
- 1 teaspoon of fresh peeled ginger, 1 teaspoon of gluten-free reduced sodium tamari

- Dash cayenne pepper (or more depending on desired degree of heat)
- 2 tablespoons of cilantro, plus more for garnish, chopped
- 2 cups of cooked chicken breast, shredded
- 10 ounces of mixed salad greens juice from a lemon, 2 tablespoons of extra virgin olive oil
- Sea salt and pepper to taste, 2 avocados

Directions:

- Blend tahini, vinegar, lime juice, ginger, garlic, tamari, spices, & cilantro until you have a liquid dressing.
- Place shredded chicken in a bowl, add dressing and toss to coat.
- In a large salad bowl, place lettuce, lemon juice, oil, salt, and pepper to taste and mix so that lettuce is coated. Divide among 4 plates.
- Halve avocados and remove pits. Place about 2 cups of chicken salad in each avocado (carve a little avocado meat out if you need more room). Garnish with extra cilantro.
- Serve over salad greens. Spoon leftover chicken onto salad. Enjoy immediately or store in the refrigerator, covered, for 3 days.

Day 5 Dinner: Salmon Veggie Kebab

(Recipe by Dr. Mark Hyman, an American physician and author, as well as the founder and medical director of The UltraWellness Center)

Ingredients:

- 1 onion, cut into large chunks
- 1 red or yellow pepper, seeded and cut into 1-inch chunks 12 button or cremini mushrooms, stems removed
- 1 zucchini, sliced into half-moons
- 16 ounces of fresh salmon, cut into 1-inch cubes
- ¼ cup of olive oil
- 1 tablespoon of chopped fresh thyme 2 cloves of crushed garlic
- ¼ cup of almond butter
- 1 tablespoon of apple cider vinegar
- ½ chili pepper seeded, 2 tablespoons of lime juice, 8 ounces of water
- 4 12-inch skewers, soaked in water
- Salt and freshly ground black pepper, to taste

Directions:

- Alternate the vegetables and salmon on each skewer.
- Combine olive oil, thyme, and crushed garlic in a large flat baking dish and add the skewers; marinate for 30 minutes or more.
- Prepare the grill.
- While waiting, combine the almond butter, apple cider vinegar, chili, lime juice, and water in the blender and blend until smooth. Season the kebabs with salt and pepper.
- Cook on the grill for 8–10 minutes until the kebabs are cooked.

Day 5 Dessert: Chocolate Avocado Mousse

Ingredients:
- 1 avocado peeled and pitted
- ¼ cup of raw organic cacao powder
- ¼ can of coconut cream
- Dash of cinnamon
- Raw honey to taste

Directions:
- Blend the avocado, cacao powder, coconut cream, Sprinkle dash of cinnamon, and honey. Chill in individual bowls. Top with shredded coconut anf fresh berries and serve.

Day 6 Breakfast: Turkey and Egg Frittata

Ingredients: Serves 1–2
- 2½ tbsp of coconut oil
- ¼ lb of ground turkey
- ½ tsp of curry powder
- ⅛ cups of grated onion, 3 eggs
- Pinch of salt
- Pinch of pepper

Directions:
- Preheat the oven to 425 degrees.
- In a small ovenproof pan, heat ½ tbsp of oil over high heat.
- Add ground turkey, curry powder, and grated onion and cook until the turkey is no longer pink, for about 3 to 4 minutes.
- Meanwhile, beat together eggs, and a pinch of salt and pepper. Add the egg mixture to the pan, lower the heat to medium-high, and cook for 2 minutes or until eggs begin to set.
- Transfer to the oven and cook until the eggs fully set, for about 5 minutes.

Day 6 Lunch: Greek Salad with Shrimp or Chicken

Ingredients: Serves 4
- 1 large cucumber, washed and dried, diced into ¼–½-inch pieces (about 2 cups)
- 1 small red onion, peeled, washed, diced into ¼-in pieces (about ¾ cup chopped)

- 1 large red bell pepper, washed and dried, seeds removed, roughly chopped (about 1¼ cups chopped)
- ½ cup of pitted olives, chopped
- 6 oz of dark leafy greens of choice
- 1-2 lbs of grilled shrimp or chicken

Dressing Ingredients:
- 2 cloves garlic, peeled, finely minced
- 1 tsp of dried oregano
- 1 tsp of Dijon mustard
- 1½ tsp of apple cider vinegar or red wine vinegar
- 2 tbsp of olive oil

Directions:
- In a medium-sized bowl, toss the salad ingredients.
- In a closed container like a mason jar, add all dressing ingredients, close lid, and shake to mix.
- Mix dressing, add it to the salad, and toss salad Top with cooked shrimp or chicken.

Day 6 Dinner: Honey Macadamia Halibut

(recipe from Institute for Integrative Nutrition)

Ingredients: Serves 2
- Two 4-6 oz of filets of halibut 1 inch thick, ¼ cup of raw macadamia nuts
- 2 tablespoons of raw honey, 1 tablespoon of coconut oil

Directions:
- Chop nuts finely, spread on baking sheet and cook for about 5-7 minutes in oven on 350 degrees until golden brown.
- Heat oil in skillet.
- Sprinkle salt and pepper on both sides of halibut. Cook first side over medium heat for 4 minutes. Flip and cook other side for 3 minutes.
- While fish is in the pan, spread a layer of honey on the fish and add a layer of nuts on top. Flip over and cook for 2 minutes, while you add honey and nuts to the other side. Flip again and cook for two minutes.

- Halibut is cooked when the meat is no longer translucent.
- Remove from heat and serve.

Day 6 Dinner: Baked Carrots

Ingredients: Serves 2–4
- 6 organic carrots peeled and sliced into a shape like fries
- 1-2 tablespoons of coconut oil or avocado oil, salt to taste
- Dill seasoning to taste

Directions:
- Preheat oven to 425° F.
- Toss carrots in a bowl to evenly distribute the oil and seasoning and toss with tongs.
- Spread carrot fries on a baking sheet.
- Bake until crispy (depends on thickness and oven) for 30-45 minutes.
- Use your smell and check on them to gauge readiness. The smaller pieces will get crispier.

Day 6 Dessert: Key Lime Coconut Milk Popsicles

Ingredients: 6 popsicles

- 1 can of organic coconut milk (full fat)
- Juice of 1 lime, zest of 1 lime
- 3-4 tablespoons of raw honey
- Optional: add in fresh chopped mint leaves

Directions:

- Whisk ingredients in a bowl.
- Adjust for sweetness desired. Pour into popsicle molds.
- Freeze for 4-6 hours.

Day 7 Breakfast: Fruit Salad with Coconut Yogurt

Ingredients: Serves 2
- ½ cup of organic blueberries
- ½ cup of organic strawberries, 1 cut organic melon
- 20 organic grapes
- 1 organic apple or pear 1 organic kiwi
- 1 organic cut pineapple
- Toppings: finely shredded coconut 1 cup of organic coconut yogurt

Directions:
- Wash and mix all fruit.
- Add shredded coconut.

Day 7 Lunch: Turkey Cutlets

Ingredients: Serves 4
- 1 lb of organic turkey cutlets sliced thinly, 1 tablespoon macadamia nut oil, salt, garlic powder, pepper to taste

Directions:
- Season turkey cutlets with salt, pepper, garlic powder. Heat a sauté pan on high and once hot, add oil.
- Carefully add turkey once oil bubbles to pan and cook for a few minutes until cooked on each side.
- Outside should be nicely browned and opaue.
- Serve with raw carrot salad.

Day 7 Lunch: Raw carrot salad

(recipe from Kate Deering in the book "How to Heal Your Metabolism")

Ingredients: Serves 2
- 2 raw medium carrots
- ½ tablespoon of melted coconut oil

- ½ tablespoon of white vinegar
- Salt to taste

Directions:
- Grate carrots lengthwise in a small bowl Mix in melted coconut oil and vinegar.
- Add salt.
- Outside should be nicely browned and opaque. Serve with raw carrot salad.

Day 7 Dinner: Paleo Lasagna
(recipe from Primal Palate)

Ingredients: Serves 4
- 1 lb of grass-fed ground beef
- 1 cup of organic Green Bell Peppers, chopped, 1 cup of organic onion, chopped
- 1 tbsp of fresh basil, 1 tbsp of parsley
- 1 tbsp of fresh oregano, or dried, 1 zucchini, sliced thinly
- 1¼ cup of white, raw mushrooms, sliced, 15 oz of tomato sauce, no salt added
- 3 cloves of minced garlic
- 6 oz of tomato paste, no salt added. 1 tsp of salt and pepper, to taste

Directions:
- Brown the ground beef in a large pot over medium heat, stirring frequently.
- Add in garlic, onion, and green pepper, and continue to sauté for 5 minutes.
- Stir in tomato paste and tomato sauce.
- Add in parsley, basil, oregano, salt and pepper, continue to stir. Bring sauce to a light boil, then remove from heat.

- Grease a 9" × 13" baking dish with coconut oil.
- Place a thin layer (½ inch) of the sauce in the baking dish.
- Layer zucchini and mushrooms over sauce, and repeat, alternating layering of sauce, then zucchini and mushrooms. Bake lasagne at 325°F for 15 minutes, covered with foil.
- After 15 minutes, remove foil, increase temperature to 350°F, and bake for an additional 15 minutes.

Day 7 Dessert: Healthy Crunch Bars

Ingredients:
- ½ cup of raw organic pumpkin seeds (sprouted if possible)
- ½ cup of raw organic sunflower seeds (sprouted if possible)
- ½ cup of shredded organic coconut
- 1 tsp of cinnamon
- 1 cup of organic shredded carrots
- ½ cup of freeze-dried organic pear, 2 organic eggs
- ¼ cup of raw organic honey, ¼ cup of organic coconut oil

Directions:
- Heat oven to 325 degrees.
- Grind up seeds to make seed meal.

- Put everything in the food processor except the coconut oil. Keep the texture coarse.
- Spread the mixture on parchment paper-lined cookie sheet. Spread melted coconut oil on the parchment paper.
- Spread the dough with hands keeping it ¼ inch thick. Cut into bars.
- Bake for 15–20 minutes.
- Remove from oven and spread apart more and bake for another 15–20 minutes.

(sprouting seeds makes them more easily digestible)

Day 8 Breakfast: Chia Seed Pudding

Ingredients: Serves 4
- 2 cups of organic blueberries
- ¾ cup of coconut milk from can (full fat)
- 2–3 tablespoons of raw honey
- ¼ teaspoon of sea salt
- ½ teaspoon of real vanilla extract
- ½ teaspoon of cinnamon
- ½ cup of chia seed
- ½ cup of unsweetened, shredded coconut, ½ teaspoon of finely grated lemon zest

Directions:
- Blend 1 cup of blueberries with coconut milk. Add salt, vanilla, cinnamon, lemon zest and chia seed to a bowl. Pour in blueberry mixture and stir to combine. Seal in an airtight container in the fridge for 12 hours or overnight.
- When ready, give pudding a stir. Divide into 4 small bowls and top with coconut, fresh berries, nuts, etc.

Day 8 Lunch: Tahini Chicken Wraps

Ingredients: Yields 4 Wraps
- 4 organic corn or coconut tortillas
- ¼ cup of tahini
- 4 leaves of organic romaine lettuce
- 1 lb of organic boneless chicken breast baked or roasted, 1 cup of grated organic carrot
- ¼ cup of organic raisins
- Salt and pepper to taste

Directions:

- Spread tahini on tortillas.
- Place one piece of lettuce in tortilla. Evenly divide sliced chicken among wraps. Sprinkle grated carrots.
- Sprinkle salt and pepper to taste. Scatter raisins on top.
- Roll wrap closed.

Day 8 Dinner: Coconut Curry with Fish

(Recipe from Dr. Mark Hyman)

Ingredients: Serves 4

- Four 4–6-ounce cod filets

Ingredients for Coconut Curry:

- 3 tablespoons of coconut butter, 1 teaspoon of mustard seeds
- 1 teaspoon of fenugreek seeds
- 1–2 fresh chilies, thinly sliced
- 1-inch piece ginger root, peeled and coarsely chopped, 2 cloves of minced garlic
- 6 curry leaves
- 2 medium onions, coarsely diced
- ½ teaspoon of chili powder
- ½ teaspoon of turmeric
- 6 medium tomatoes, seeded and coarsely diced, or 1 (15-ounce) can low-sodium diced tomatoes
- 4 cups of low-sodium vegetable stock
- ½ cup of unsweetened coconut milk salt, to taste

Ingredients for Vegetables:
- 1 cup of cauliflower florets, 1 cup of sliced zucchini
- 1 cup of chopped baby bok choy, 1 cup of spinach

Ingredients for Garnish:
- ½ cup of chopped raw almonds
- ½ bunch of fresh cilantro, leaves pulled

Directions: Prepare the Curry Sauce:
- In a large saucepan, heat 2 tablespoons of the oil over medium heat.
- Add the mustard seeds and reduce the heat to low. When the seeds start to pop, add the fenugreek, chillies, ginger, garlic, and curry leaves if using.
- Stir for about 3 minutes, then add the diced onions and cook 5 minutes until they are soft and slightly brown.
- Add the chili powder, turmeric, diced tomatoes, and vegetable stock and bring to a boil. Reduce heat and simmer for 15 minutes.
- Add the coconut milk and simmer for an additional 5 minutes. Season with salt, and stir in the remaining coconut butter just before serving.

Prepare the Fish
- Add fish to the sauce and cook for an additional 5-7 minutes, or until the fish is opaque inside.

Prepare the Vegetables:
- Bring ½ cup of water to a boil in a saucepan or sauté pan.
- If you are using a saucepan, place the vegetables in a metal or bamboo steamer inside the pan and cover the pan with a lid.
- Steam for 3-5 minutes until the vegetables are tender and soft. If you are using a sauté pan, place the vegetable.

Day 8 Dessert: Salted Dark Chocolate Nut & Fruit Clusters

Ingredients: Serves 20

- 12 oz of organic dark chocolate (no soy)
- 1 teaspoon of organic coconut oil
- 1½ cup of toasted organic almonds, whole
- ½ cup of whole dried organic cranberries or cherries, coarse Himalayan salt

Directions:

- Melt chocolate and coconut oil on stovetop, heating for 1 minute & 30 seconds. If necessary, heat until melted in 30 second increments.
- Stir until smooth and fully melted.
- Stir in nuts and dried fruit to soak up the entire melted chocolate.
- Drop spoonfuls of mixture onto a wax paper or parchment paper-lined baking sheet.
- Sprinkle with a touch of salt.
- Place the pan into freezer and let harden.

Day 9 Breakfast: Vegetable Frittata

Ingredients: Serves 3–4
- 8 pasture-raised eggs, beaten
- 1 tbsp of coconut oil
- ½ cup of finely diced sweet onion
- ½ cup of finely diced sweet bell pepper, ½ cup of finely diced zucchini
- Salt, to taste
- Pepper, to taste
- ½ cup of fresh spinach leaves, stems removed

Directions:
- In a 10-inch sauté pan, add oil and heat the pan. When the pan becomes hot, add onion, pepper, zucchini and season to taste with salt and pepper, stirring frequently.
- Sauté until vegetables are just becoming tender. Add fresh spinach and cook until wilted.
- Add beaten eggs evenly around vegetables and begin to gently fold sides inward from rim of pan where the eggs begin to cook. Finish cooking the top of the eggs by putting the pan under a preheated broiler or by flipping the frittata over in the pan. The pan can also go in a preheated 350 degree F oven until the eggs are done.

Day 9 Lunch: Grilled Pepper Steak Salad

(Recipe from Dr. Mark Hyman)

Ingredients: Serves 4

- 4 (5-ounce) pieces flank steak (or steak of your choice), 1 tbsp of extra-virgin olive oil
- ¼ cup of freshly ground black pepper
- ½ tsp of salt
- 1 tbsp of chopped fresh parsley

Directions:

- Prepare the grill or use a grill pan.
- Brush each piece of steak with the olive oil.
- Combine the peppers and salt in a small bowl, and rub the steaks with the seasoning mix; let sit for five minutes.
- Grill the steaks for about 3–4 minutes on each side (or to desired doneness).
- Let stand for 5 minutes before slicing.
- Sprinkle with chopped parsley and serve with salad of your choice: arugula, mesclun mix, etc.

Day 9 Dinner: Gluten-Free Fish Sticks Served with Green Salad

Ingredients: Serves 4

- 1 lb of wild cod fillets from Norway or Northeast Arctic, 2 large pasture-raised eggs beaten

- ⅓ cup of organic rice flour, ⅓ cup of potato starch
- 1 cup of gluten-free bread crumbs, ½ teaspoon of Himalayan sea salt, ¼ teaspoon of pepper
- Organic olive oil spray

Directions:

- Preheat oven to 400° F.
- Grease cookie sheet with olive oil spray. Cut fish into ½-¾-inch-wide strips.
- In a bowl, beat the eggs with a fork until the white no longer holds together.
- In another bowl, combine the rice flour, potato starch, salt and pepper.
- Place breadcrumbs in a third bowl.
- Working with several pieces at a time, coat the fish with flour, dredge in the beaten egg, and then coat with breadcrumbs.
- Place on the baking sheet and bake for 10–15 minutes. Serve with green salad.

Day 9 Dessert: Grilled Mango and Peaches with Honey

Ingredients: Serves 3

- 2–3 sweet ripe organic mangoes and peaches sliced
- 2 tablespoons of raw organic honey, cinnamon to taste

Directions:

- Heat a grill pan on stovetop.
- Place fruit halves face down, cooking for about 5 minutes or until nice grill marks.
- Flip fruit halfway through cooking, Add honey and cinnamon.
- Cook for another 1–2 minutes.

Day 10 Breakfast: Smoked Salmon on Paleo Bread

Ingredients for bread:
- ¼ teaspoon of sea salt
- ½ teaspoon of baking soda, 5 pasture-raised eggs
- 1 tablespoon of coconut oil, 1 tablespoon of raw honey
- tablespoon apple cider vinegar
- Optional seasonings: oregano, basil, garlic powder, and dried onion flakes
- Wild smoked salmon slices, organic avocado, sliced
- Fresh dill, capers, sliced onion

Directions:
- Preheat oven to 350° F.
- Mix dry ingredients until well blended. Add in eggs, oil, honey, and vinegar.
- Blend together or pulse in food processor.
- Transfer batter to a greased 7.5 × 3.5 magic line loaf pan.
- Bake for 30 minutes. Cool in the pan for 2 hours.

- Once cooled, slice bread, and top with avocado and add salmon, capers, dill, onions.

Day 10 Breakfast: Coconut Blueberry Smoothie

Ingredients: Serves 2
- 1.5 cups of fresh or frozen organic blueberries
- ½ cup of unsweetened organic coconut milk, 1 teaspoon of organic lime juice
- 1 teaspoon of organic raw honey
- 1 cup of ice made with filtered water

Directions:
- Blend all ingredients in blender until smooth Add more lime juice and honey if desired.

Day 10 Lunch: Turkey Burger with Lettuce Wraps

Ingredients: Serves 4
- 1 pound of organic ground turkey
- ½ sliced organic red bell pepper
- ¼ organic onion chopped
- 2 tablespoons of organic egg white
- 1 teaspoon of garlic powder
- 1 teaspoon of ginger
- 1 teaspoon of chili flakes
- 4 leaves of butter leaf organic lettuce, organic coconut oil
- Organic ketchup, organic pickles

Directions:

- Combine all ingredients in a bowl and mix well. Form into 4-ounce patties.
- Grill or fry on greased pan for 5 minutes each side until thoroughly cooked.
- Wrap in a butter leaf lettuce.
- Serve with ketchup, pickles.

Day 10 Dinner: Lamb Kabobs

Ingredients: Serves 4

- 2 lbs of organic grass-fed lamb meat cubed
- 12 wood skewers
- 2 cups of organic pearl onions
- 2 cups of organic cherry tomatoes
  1 large organic zucchini

Marinade ingredients:

- 1½ cups of organic olive oil ¼ cup of Worcestershire sauce
- ½ teaspoon of salt
- 3 tablespoons of fresh chopped parsley fresh ground pepper to taste
- ½ cup of organic wine vinegar
- 2 tablespoons of fresh minced organic garlic
- ½ cup of organic raw honey
- 2 small organic green onions sliced

Directions:

- Assemble kabobs: add to a wooden skewer the cubed raw lamb, and alternate between pearl onions, cherry tomatoes, and sliced zucchini.
- Blend all marinade ingredients in a blender except the green onion. After blended, add in the green onions.
- Marinate kabobs for 24 hours in the refrigerator.
- Grill kabobs on medium high heat for 10 minutes, rotating every 2 minutes.

Day 10 Dinner: Roasted Broccoli and Cauliflower

Ingredients: Serves 4

- 1 head of organic broccoli using only the flower part
- 1 head of organic cauliflower, using just the flower part, 3 cloves of organic minced garlic
- 5 tablespoons of organic olive oil, sea salt to taste

Directions:

- In a baking pan, arrange broccoli and cauliflower tops in a single layer.
- Sprinkle olive oil to coat veggies, and then season with salt and garlic.
- Bake in oven at 350° F for 1 hour until golden crispy appearance.

Day 10 Dessert: Lychee, Coconut, and Lime Popsicles

(recipe from Wallflower Kitchen)

Ingredients: Yields 6 popsicles
- 1 14-oz can of lychees
- 1 14-oz can of coconut milk, zest and juice of 1 lime
- 2 tablespoons of raw honey

Directions:
- Combine all ingredients in a blender and mix until well blended and smooth.
- Pour the mixture into your popsicle molds and freeze overnight or until solid.

Day 11 Breakfast: Hard-boiled Pasture-Raised Eggs with Raw Carrots and Apple slices

(great for a busy morning)

Ingredients: Serves 2
- 4 pasture-raised eggs
- 4 organic raw carrots, peeled and sliced thinly, 1 organic apple peeled and sliced, Himalayan salt to taste

Directions:
- Bring a pot of water to boil, leaving the eggs near the flame to get warm while water is boiling.
- Once boiling, drop eggs carefully in pot with a spoon and set time for 15 minutes.
- Prepare carrots and apples while waiting.
- Feel free to squeeze some fresh lemon juice on the carrots and apples to preserve.
- Remove eggs once done and dip in some cold water for 30 seconds to cool the shell.
- Then use a knife to tap the shell carefully and start to use your fingers to peel the shell off the eggs.
- Sprinkle Himalayan salt.

Day 11 Lunch: Sautéed Organic Chicken Tenders with Peanut Sauce

(recipe from Minimalist Baker)

Ingredients: Serves 4

Peanut Sauce:
- ½ cup of organic salted creamy peanut butter
- 1-2 tablespoons of coconut aminos
- 1-2 tablespoons of maple syrup or raw honey, 1 teaspoon of chili garlic sauce
- 2-3 tablespoons of lime juice
- About ¼ cup of water to thin the sauce

Directions:
- To a medium mixing bowl add peanut butter, coconut aminos, maple syrup, lime juice, chili sauce and whisk to combine. Add water a little at a time until a thick but pourable sauce is achieved.
- Taste and adjust seasonings as needed, adding more maple syrup for sweetness, chili garlic sauce (or red chili or red pepper) for heat, lime juice for acidity, or coconut aminos for saltiness. If your sauce has become too thin, add more nut butter. If it's too thick, thin with more water.
- For a fun flavor twist, add some fresh grated ginger to taste.

Ingredients: Serves 4

Organic Chicken Strips:
- 2 lbs of organic chicken tenders, raw salt, pepper to taste
- ½ tsp of garlic powder
- 2 tbsp of olive oil or fat of choice

Directions:

- Heat skillet over medium heat and when hot enough, add 2 tablespoons of oil to skillet.
- Pat dry chicken tenders and sprinkle seasoning on one side of the chicken.
- Place the chicken season side down in hot oil and brown on one side for about 4 minutes or until brown.
- Season the second side of chicken and flip over to brown it.
- Cook the chicken until internal temp of 165 degrees. Option to also grill chicken on skewers.
- Serve with peanut sauce.
- Pairs well with shaved carrot and cucumber salad.

Day 11 Dinner: Grilled Shrimp with Mango Salsa

Ingredients: Serves 6

- 12 large shrimp
- ¼ cup of extra virgin olive oil, juice from 1 organic lemon
- Sea salt and fresh pepper to taste

Salsa:

- Juice from 2 organic limes
- 2 organic diced mangoes, 1 diced organic red onion, 1 tablespoon of chili powder, ½ bunch of fresh organic cilantro leaves, chopped
- ⅟₃₄ cup of extra virgin olive oil, sea salt and pepper to taste

Directions:
- In a large bowl, toss prawns in olive oil, lemon juice, salt and pepper and let marinate for 30 minutes.
- Grill prawns on each side until opaque and pink (5 minutes).
- Add all salsa ingredients to a bowl and mix well.
- Place warm grilled prawns on a platter and top with salsa.
- Serve with grilled zucchini, onions, etc.

Day 11 Dessert: Frozen Bananas in Dark Chocolate

Ingredients:
- 2 ripe but firm bananas
- 6 ounces of dark organic chocolate
- Optional toppings: raw nuts, shredded coconut

Directions:
- Line a baking sheet with parchment paper.
- Cut bananas in half and insert popsicle stick into each half. Place on baking sheet and freeze for 15 minutes.
- Melt chocolate on double boiler and stir until smooth.
- Roll each banana in chocolate and quickly sprinkle with toppings.
- Freeze for about 30 minutes until chocolate sets.
- Serve or freeze in airtight container for up to a week.

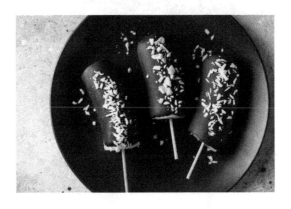

Day 12 Breakfast: Gluten-Free Blueberry Pancakes

Ingredients: Serves 6
- 1 ripe organic banana
- 2 pasture-raised eggs
- 2 tablespoons of almond meal, ½ teaspoon of vanilla extract
- ½ teaspoon of cinnamon powder, ½ cup of organic blueberries
- 1 tablespoon of organic coconut oil
- Fresh organic berries and maple syrup for topping

Directions:
- Mash up the banana with a fork in the mixing bowl. Add almond meal.
- Whisk in eggs, vanilla, and cinnamon. Stir in blueberries.
- Heat oil in a pan on a griddle.
- Ladle batter in a pan and cook each pancake for 1–2 minutes on each side or until it bubbles in the middle.
- Carefully use a spatula to flip to the other side and cook for another 1–2 minutes.
- Top with fresh berries and maple syrup.

Day 12 Breakfast: Fresh Pomegranates with Crushed Walnut Paste

Ingredients: Serves 2
- Seeds of one pomegranate, ½ cup of organic walnuts
- 1 tablespoon of raw organic honey, ½ cup of organic shredded coconut

Directions:
- Seed the pomegranate and place in a medium bowl. Put walnuts in a blender or food processor and crush until they become paste.
- Add pomegranate seeds, honey, and coconut. Spoon into small serving bowls.

Day 12 Lunch: Grass-Fed Burger

Ingredients: Serves 2–4
- 1 lb of grass-fed ground beef
- Seasoning: salt, pepper, garlic powder, oregano, onion powder. Sliced organic onion for sautéeing
- Macadamia nut oil for the pan

Directions:
- Let grass-fed beef rest at room temperature for 20 minutes.
- In a large bowl, add the grass-fed beef and season with all the seasonings to your liking.
- Form meat into patties about 1 inch thick and 3 inches in diameter.
- Heat a pan and add oil evenly to the surface.
- Once hot, add patties and cook for 4–5 minutes and then flip.
- Cook for another 3–4 minutes or until browned.
- Remove from heat and add onions in oil to sautée until soft and golden.
- Serve with sweet potato fries (recipe on next page).

Day 12 Lunch: Sweet Potato Fries

Ingredients: Serves 2–4
- 1–2 sweet potatoes, peeled and sliced into fries
- Seasoning: salt, pepper, garlic powder, paprika 1–2 tablespoons of coconut oil

Directions:
- Let grass-fed beef rest at room temperature for 20 minutes.
- Prepare this before the burgers as they take longer.
- Preheat oven to 450° F.
- Lay fries on a parchment-lined baking sheet.
- Sprinkle with oil and seasonings.
- Bake for 20–30 minutes until golden.

Day 12 Dinner: Cod Cakes

Ingredients: Serves 4

- 4 (4–6 ounce) cod fillets
- ½ cup of macadamia nuts, 1 pasture-raised egg
- 1 tablespoon of chopped fresh thyme, 1 tablespoon of chopped parsley
- ¼ cup of diced red onion
- 1 tablespoon of lemon zest, 1 teaspoon of lemon juice
- 1 teaspoon of Dijon mustard, pinch of cayenne
- ½ teaspoon of salt
- ½ teaspoon of freshly ground black pepper, 1 tablespoon of macadamia nut oil
- Salad greens

Directions:

- Fill a steamer or a saucepan with about ¼ inch of water, and bring to a boil. Add the cod fillets, cover, and cook on medium heat for about 7 minutes or until translucent. Let cool. Using a fork, break up the fish into flakes.
- In a spice grinder or food processor, grind macadamia nuts to the size of medium-size breadcrumbs. Alternatively, you can place the nuts in a plastic baggy and crush them using a rolling pin.
- In a large bowl whisk the egg adding in the herbs, onion, lemon juice, and lemon zest. Add the fish flakes mustard, cayenne, salt, and pepper. Form into four patties. Spread the ground pumpkin seeds or macadamia nuts onto a plate and coat the patties on all sides.
- Heat the olive oil in a sauté pan on medium heat. Cook the cod cakes for 3 minutes on each side.
- Assemble the dish: Serve each cod cake alongside or on top of the greens, garnish with tomato wedges, and drizzle with olive oil and lemon juice.

Day 12 Dessert: Gluten-Free Cake Pops

Ingredients: Serves 8

- 1 box of gluten-free cake mix
- ½ cup of melted coconut butter, ¾ cup coconut milk
- Vanilla to taste
- Organic coconut oil spray Cake pop trays

Ruth's gluten free dairy free cake pops

Directions:

- Heat oven to 350° F Combine butter, milk, vanilla, and cake; mix in a bowl.
- Mix on medium speed for 2 minutes until well mixed.
- Spray cake pop trays with the coconut oil.
- Pour batter into trays; bake for 30 minutes.
- Cake pops are done when a toothpick inserted into them comes out clear.
- Add popsicle sticks into center and serve.

Day 13 Breakfast: Tomato Egg Dish

Ingredients: Serves 3

- 6 pasture-raised eggs
- 2 organic tomatoes peeled & cut into quarters
- 1 lb of organic red peppers peeled and cut into quarters
- 6 garlic cloves minced
- 1 sweet organic onion chopped finely
- 1 tablespoon of organic tomato paste 2 tablespoons of sweet paprika
- 1 tablespoon of macadamia nut oil; sea salt and pepper to taste

Directions:

- Place all ingredients except eggs into a saucepan and bring to simmer uncovered on low flame for 30 minutes.
- It should turn into a thick tomato sauce, so stir every five minutes.
- Remove from heat and stir so it is thick.
- Place mixture into a greased 12-inch frying pan.
- Break open each egg a few inches apart from each other.
- Cook on flame on medium heat for five minutes (if you like runny eggs, it may need as much time).
- Cover pan, but continue to check and remove from heat.

Day 13 Breakfast: Bacon-Wrapped Figs

Ingredients: Serves 2

- 6 large organic figs, washed and peeled
- 6 slices of pasture-raised nitrate-free bacon, 1 teaspoon of cinnamon
- ½ teaspoon of chili powder, salt to taste
- Toothpicks

Directions:

- Heat toaster oven to broil and line toaster oven tray with foil. Wrap each fig in a strip of bacon and secure with a large toothpick.
- Season with salt, pepper, cinnamon, chili powder Place prepared figs on a toaster oven tray.

- Bake for 10-12 minutes or until bacon is crisp and figs are tender.
- Remove from oven and transfer to a serving plate. Serve warm.

Day 13 Lunch: Avocado, Cucumber, Turkey Sandwich

Ingredients: Serves 2
- 1 organic avocado sliced
- 1 medium organic cucumber sliced, 2 tablespoons of avocado mayonnaise, 1 tablespoon of lemon juice
- Salt and pepper to taste, 4 slices of paleo bread
- 8-10 ounces of sliced organic antibiotic-free turkey breast

Directions:
- Toast bread.
- Spread mayonnaise on one slice of bread.
- Add avocado cucumber and turkey.
- Season to liking.
- Add other slice of bread.

Day 13 Dinner: Maple Chili-Glazed Pork Medallions

Ingredients: Serves 4
- 1 lb of organic pork medallion trimmed and cut into 1-inch medallions
- ¼ cup of organic apple cider
- 1 tablespoon of organic maple syrup, 2 teaspoons of macadamia nut oil
- 1 teaspoon of chili powder
- 1 teaspoon of apple cider vinegar, ½ teaspoon of himalayan salt
- ⅛ teaspoon of ground chipotle pepper

Directions:
- Mix chili powder, salt, chipotle in a small bowl. Sprinkle over both sides of pork.
- Heat oil in a large skillet over medium-high heat.
- Add pork and cook until golden, 1-2 minutes per side. Add cider, syrup, and vinegar to the pan.
- Bring to a boil, scraping up and browned bits.
- Reduce heat to medium and cook for 1-3 minutes, turning pork occasionally to coat until the sauce is reduced to a thick glaze.
- Serve pork drizzled with glaze.

Day 13 Dinner: Baked Zucchini Chips

Ingredients: Serves 2
- Organic extra virgin olive oil cooking spray, 1 organic zucchini, thinly sliced
- 1 teaspoon of salt
- ½ teaspoon of pepper

Directions:
- Heat oven to 200° F.
- Line cookie sheet with cooking parchment paper. Spray paper with olive oil cooking spray.
- Place zucchini slices on cookie sheet in single layer. Spray tops with cooking spray.
- Sprinkle evenly with salt and pepper.
- Bake for 2 hours, rotating cookie sheet after 1 hour.
- After 1 hour 30 minutes, check zucchini every 10 minutes to avoid burning.
- Remove from oven and place on cooling rack. Serve warm or cool.
- Store in airtight container.

Day 13 Dinner: Banana and Chocolate Pudding

Ingredients: Serves 2
- 3 bananas peeled (yellow with few spots is great, but not too ripe)
- ½ avocado
- ¼ cup of smooth almond butter, 4–5 tablespoons of raw cacao powder
- 1 teaspoon of vanilla extract, pinch of sea salt

Directions:
- Add all ingredients into a food processor and process until smooth.
- Portion the pudding into a container and chill in the fridge for an hour or so (but can also be eaten right away).
- Remove from the fridge, add toppings you wish.
- The pudding is best enjoyed if eaten within 12–24 hours of being prepared.

Day 14 Breakfast: BLT Egglets

Ingredients: Serves 4
- 8 hard organic boiled eggs
- 6 strips of nitrate-free bacon, 3 crisp lettuce leaves
- 2 small vine-ripe tomatoes, mayonnaise to taste
- Vegan cheese slices to taste

Directions:
- Cook the bacon.
- Peel the eggs and cut in half.
- Add mayonnaise, lettuce, tomato, bacon, and vegan cheese.

Day 14 Lunch: Bento Box Lunch

Ingredients: Serves 1
- Organic chickpeas rinsed
- Organic nitrate-free sliced turkey, rolled organic raw carrots
- Sliced organic cucumbers, seaweed chips
- 1 ripe avocado, cubed
- Organic sulfite-free dried fruit

Directions:
- Fill bento box with all ingredients.
- You can be creative here and even add leftovers.

Day 14 Dinner: Shrimp Avocado Salad

Ingredients: Serves 2

- ½ pound of shrimp, peeled and deveined, ½ tsp of chili powder
- 1 tbsp of extra virgin olive oil, ½ red pepper, diced
- 1 ripe avocado, cubed, 1 tbsp of lime juice
- 6 cherry tomatoes sliced in half Cilantro to taste
- Salt to taste

Directions:

- Rinse shrimp and pat dry. Sprinkle shrimp with salt and chili powder.
- Heat ½ tbsp of the olive oil in a skillet on medium heat. Carefully place shrimp in a pan and sear on each side for about 2 minutes until cooked through. Remove from heat and set aside to cool.
- Combine all vegetables in a serving bowl and toss with the remaining olive oil and lime juice. Gently fold in shrimp and add a little extra virgin olive oil.

Avocado Salad Dressing

Ingredients: Serves 4

- ½ avocado
- Juice from ½ lemon
- ½ garlic clove grated
- 1 tbsp of scallions minced, 1 tbsp of fresh basil
- Salt and pepper to taste

Directions:

- Place all ingredients in food blender and puree until smooth. If necessary, add water to desired texture/ viscosity.
- Top on any salad.

Day 14 Dessert: Watermelon Pizza

(recipe from Choosing Chia)

Ingredients:

- 1 watermelon
- 1 cup of coconut yogurt, ½ cup of strawberries, sliced in half
- ½ cup of raspberries, ½ cup of cherries, ½ cup of blueberries
- ½ cup of pomegranate seeds
- Honey or maple syrup (optional)

Directions:

- Using a sharp knife, cut off a slice of watermelon right down the middle, about 2–3 inches thick.
- Using a spatula, spread an even layer of your yogurt around the watermelon leaving a bit of empty space at the top. (where your "pizza crust" is).
- Layer your fresh fruit on top as you please. You can add as little or as many toppings as you like!
- Drizzle with honey or maple syrup for a little extra sweetness if desired.

Notes

Use a sharp knife to cut the watermelon, to get nice even cuts. Use any berries or fruit you love to top this watermelon pizza

My son Jonah

Food Shopping List

Staples to always have
- Almond cheese (no soy or vegetable oils added)
- Applegate Farms frozen sausages and bacon antibiotic and nitrate free
- Bone broth
- Chia pudding
- Gluten- and dairy-free paleo cake mixes and pancake/waffle mixes
- Gluten-free granola
- Grass-fed ground beef
- Green powder mixes
- Himalayan sea salt
- Milk made from hemp, oats, rice, almond, coconut
- Miso soup mix
- Organic almond butter and cashew butter
- Organic almonds and cashews
- Organic aloe vera juice
- Organic bottled salad dressing without seed oils
- Organic canned beans
- Organic carrots
- Organic chia seeds
- Organic coconut aminos (good substitute for soy sauce)
- Organic coconut yogurt
- Organic corn chips
- Organic flax crackers
- Organic flax seed bread
- Organic flaxseeds
- Organic fresh garlic
- Organic fresh ginger

- Organic frozen fruit
- Organic fruits and veggies
- Organic gluten-free pasta
- Organic hemp seeds
- Organic herbal tea (looseleaf or BPA free)
- Organic ice creams made from coconut milk and natural sugars
- Organic ketchup
- Organic lemons, limes
- Organic mayonnaise made with olive oil or avocado oil instead of soybean oil
- Organic meats
- Organic olive oil, coconut oil, avocado oil, and macadamia nut oil
- Organic pasture-raised eggs, Soy & Corn free (Araucana hens have a very orange yolk)
- Organic raw/sprouted nuts
- Organic raw honey
- Organic rice crackers
- Organic roasted seaweed
- Organics easonings: Basil, Cinnamon, Garlic Powder, Onion Powder, Oregano, Pepper, Thyme
- Organic sea vegetables
- Organic shredded coconut flakes
- Organic tahini
- Organic vegetables and fruits
- Pasture-Raised chicken (soy and corn free)
- Spring Water in Glass

Important Nutrition Guides and Cookbooks

A *Parent's Guide to Childhood Obesity: A Road Map to Good Health* by the American Academy of Pediatrics

Candle 79 Cookbook: Modern Vegan Classics from New York's Premier Sustainable Restaurant by Joy Pierson, Angel Ramos, and Jorge Pineda

Dinner with Dad: How One Man Braved Traffic, Battled Picky Eaters, and Found His Way Back to the Family Table by Cameron Stracher

Eat Right 4 Your Type By Dr. Peter J. D'Adamo

Fast Food Nation: What The All-American Meal is Doing to the World by Eric Schlosser

Feed Your Kids Well: How to Help Your Child Lose Weight and Get Healthy by Fred Pescatore, M.D.

Great Parties for Kids: Fabulous and Creative Idea's for Children Aged 0–10 by Charlotte Packer and Rose Hammick

Jane Brody's Nutrition Book: A Lifetime Guide to Good Eating for Better Health and Weight Control by Jane Brody

Mindless Eating: Why We Eat More than We Think by Brian Wansink More Home Cooking: A Writer Returns to the Kitchen by Laurie Colwin

Naked Chocolate: The Astonishing Truth About The World's Greatest Food by David Wolfe and Shazzie

Naturally Thin: by Bethenny Frankel

Near a Thousand Tables: A History of Food by Felipe Fernandez-Armesto

Real Food for Healthy Kids by Tracey Seaman and Tanya Wenmen Steel

Superfoods: The Food and Medicine of the Future by David Wolfe

The Cleaner Plate Club: Raising Healthy Eaters One Meal at a Time by Beth Bader and Ali Benjamin

The Kids Pick-A-Party Book by Penny Warner

The Surprising Power of Family Meals: How Eating Together Makes Us Smarter, Stronger, Healthier and Happier by Miriam Weinstein

Websites

ALCAT Test (www.alcat.com) information to understand the ALCAT food sensitivity test

Beaba (www.beabausa.com) baby food maker

Bon Appetit (www.bonappetit.com) great resource for recipes

Dr. Fred Pescatore, MD (www.drpescatore.com) natural physician

Dr. Joseph Mercola (www.mercola.com) holistic physician

Dr. Leo Galland (www.drgalland.com)

Dr. Peter D'Adamo (www.4yourtype.com) naturopathic physician

Dr. Robert Pastore, Ph.D. CNS (www.drrobertpastore.com)

Earthbound Farms (www.ebfarm.com) non-GMO and organic salads, fruits, and vegetables

Eden Foods, Inc (www.edenfoods.com) specialty organic products

Eat Wild (www.eatwild.com) source for local farms, organic produce, pasture-raised eggs, grass-fed, pasture-raised animals

Exotic Superfoods (www.exoticsuperfoods.com) organic and raw coconut meat and water

Feeding America (www.feedingamerica.org) information on where your local food banks are

Food babe- (www.foodbabe.com) healthy fun recipes

Food recipes (www.food.com) making art with food

Food for my family (www.foodformyfamily.com) great advice on how to get your kids in the kitchen

Four Seasons Produce, Inc (www.fsproduce.com) organic produce

Greenbar Collective (www.greenbar.biz) organic and eco-friendly liquors

Kids Health (www.kidshealth.org)

Laura McDonald Health (www.lauramcdonaldhealth.com) health coach and fitness blogger

Lunch Lessons School Food System Consultants (www.lunchlessonsllc.com)

Maine Coast Sea Vegetables (www.seaveg.com)

Navitas Naturals (www.navitasorganics.com) organic cashews, cacao, wakame, nori fruits, and berries

Nutrition Data (www.nutritiondata.com)

Nutrition for Kids (www.nutritionforkids.com)

Nutrition Intuition (https://www.nutritionin2ition.com/)

Organic Consumer Association (www.organicconsumers.org) information, advocacy, recipes, and more about lively organically

Priscilla Woolworth Eco Friendly General Store (www.priscillawoolworth.com)

Reusable bags (www.1bagatatime.com)

South River Miso (www.southrivermiso.com) organic miso products

Sunfood Superfoods (www.sunfood.com) shop for highest quality raw foods

Teris Kitchen (www.teriskitchen.com) great advice on a well-stocked kitchen

The Eat Well Guide (www.eatwellguide.org)

The Edible Schoolyard (www.edibleschoolyard.org)

The National Institutes of Health's MedlinePlus (www.medlineplus.gov/medlineplus/nutrition.htm1)

The Institute for Integrative Nutrition (www.integrativenutrition.com)

The Weston A Price Foundation (www.westonaprice.org) resource for traditional nutrition & health

TruRoots (www.truroots.com) organic sprouted and whole grains and beans

Wholesome Baby Food (www.wholesomebabyfood.com)

Kids Cooking Classes

www.foodliteracycenter.org/

www.kids-table.com/virtual-classes

www.youngchefsacademy.com

www.kidscookinggreen.com/

www.surlatable.com/cooking-classes/kids-teens-cooking-series/

www.raddishkids.com/

Food Diary

MyFitnessPal – A free smartphone application to log in your food with the option to upgrade for premium membership

YouAte.com – An easy-to-use food journaling app designed to help you establish and maintain a healthy eating habit

Market Resources

Eat Wild – (www.eatwild.com)

Local Harvest (www.localharvest.org)

The United States Department of Agriculture (www.ams.usda.gov/farmersmarkets)

Sustainable Agriculture Research and Education (www.sare.org)

National Sustainable Agriculture Information Services (www.sustainableagriculture.net)

Food Sensitivity Resources

Food Allergy Initiative (www.foodallergy.org)

The National Digestive Diseases Information (www.niddk.nih.gov/health-information/digestive-diseases)

Peanut Allergy (www.peanutallergy.com)

A Celiac and Gluten-Free Resource (www.celiac.com)

Almond milk recipes (www.minimalistbaker.com/how-to-make-almond-milk/)

(www.almondcow.co/products/almond-cow-milk-machine)

Sugar Alternatives

Coconut sugar – from sap of coconut flowers.

Dates – fruit that is naturally dry, high in selenium, magnesium.

Date sugar – finely ground in granulated form.

Honey (raw, organic, unfiltered) – most nutrient-dense form, beneficial enzymes, minerals, vitamins, immune benefits.

Lucuma – A dried exotic fruit. Has a nutty, maple flavor and is rich in nutrients. The lucuma has particularly dry flesh which possesses a unique flavor of maple and sweet potato, high levels of antioxidants, carotene, vitamin B3, and other B vitamins.

Maple syrup – boiled-down maple tree sap containing many minerals.

Maple sugar – sap of sugar boiled for longer then maple syrup once water evaporates, twice as sweet as standard granulated sugar but less refined.

Molasses and muscovado sugar – most nutritious sweetener derived from sugar cane or sugar beet made from clarifying and blending extracted juice, blackstrap good source of calcium, iron, magnesium, and potassium.

Monk fruit extract – exotic fruit called buddha fruit of southeast asia that gets sweetness from antioxidants called mogrosides. Zero calories and up to 250 times sweeter than table sugar.

Sucanat – a variety of whole cane sugar that has minerals and antioxidants.

Sources & Organizations

Throughout the book we have relied on these valuable sources:

Chapter 1: Growing Pains and Frozen Dinners.

p. 4 Pesticides harmful effects:

1) EPA. NIEHS/EPA Children's Environmental Health and Disease Prevention Research Centers Impact Report.

2) Liu J, Zhao F, Xu Y, Qiu J, Qian Y. Gut Flora-Mediated Metabolic Health, the Risk Produced by Dietary Exposure to Acetamiprid and Tebuconazole. Foods. 2021 Apr 12;10(4):835. doi: 10.3390/foods10040835. PMID: 33921314; PMCID: PMC8070257

3) Gore AC, Chappell VA, Fenton SE, et al. EDC-2: The Endocrine Society's Second Scientific Statement on Endocrine-Disrupting Chemicals. *Endocrine Reviews.* 2015;36(6):E1-E150. doi:10.1210/er.2015-1010

p. 4 Farmers could cut pesticides and not lose production: Lechenet, M., Dessaint, F., Py, G. et al. Reducing pesticide use while preserving crop productivity and profitability on arable farms. Nature Plants 3, 17008 (2017). https://doi.org/10.1038/nplants.2017.8

Chapter 2: Finding My Way in an Unhealthy World of Excess.

p. 9 Soda/artificial sweetener disrupts gut: Nettleton JE, Reimer RA, Shearer J. Reshaping the gut microbiota: Impact of low calorie sweeteners and the link to insulin resistance? Physiol Behav. 2016 Oct 1;164(Pt B):488–493. doi: 10.1016/j.physbeh.2016.04.029. Epub 2016 Apr 15. PMID: 27090230.

p. 10 Lactose intolerance prevalence: Definition & Facts for Lactose Intolerance. NIDDK | National Institute of Diabetes and Digestive and Kidney Diseases. https://www.niddk.nih.gov/health-information/digestive-diseases/lactose- intolerance/definition-facts. Published December 9, 2021.

p. 11 Ancient Einkorn flour nutrition benefits superior to modern wheat: Antognoni F, Mandrioli R, Bordoni A, et al. Integrated Evaluation of the Potential Health Benefits of Einkorn-Based Breads. Nutrients. 2017;9(11):1232. Published 2017 Nov 11. doi:10.3390/nu9111232

p. 11 Einkorn ancient flour healthier than modern flour: Barone F, Laghi L, Gianotti A, et al. In Vivo Effects of Einkorn Wheat (Triticum monococcum) Bread on the Intestinal Microbiota, Metabolome, and on the Glycemic and Insulinemic Response in the Pig Model. Nutrients. 2018;11(1):16. Published 2018 Dec 20. doi:10.3390/nu11010016

p. 12 The connection between glyphosate and gluten intolerance: Samsel A, Seneff S. Glyphosate, pathways to modern diseases II: Celiac sprue and gluten intolerance. Interdiscip Toxicol. 2013;6(4):159–184. doi:10.2478/intox-2013-0026

p. 14 Non-GMO vs. Organic: Organic. Agricultural Marketing Service. Organic. Agricultural Marketing Service. Accessed July 4, 2022. https://www.ams.usda.gov/grades- standards/organic-standards

p. 14 Food sensitivities symptoms: Majsiak E, Choina M, Golicki D, Gray AM, Cukrowska B. The impact of symptoms on quality of life before and after diagnosis of coeliac disease: the results from a Polish population survey and comparison with the results from the United Kingdom. BMC Gastroenterol. 2021 Mar 4;21(1):99. doi: 10.1186/s12876-021-01673-0. PMID: 33663388; PMCID: PMC7934494.

Chapter 4: Two Boys Hungry All the Time

p. 21 Food Labels 8. Safety <a href="/taxonomy/term/816" hreflang="en">Center for F, Nutrition</a> A. Menu Labeling Requirements. U.S. Food and Drug Administration.

Accessed July 4, 2022. https://www.fda.gov/food/food-labeling-nutrition/menu-labeling- requirements

p. 22 Obesity prevalence- 7. The State of Childhood Obesity – Helping All Children Grow Up Healthy. The State of Childhood Obesity. Published October 9, 2019. Accessed July 4, 2022. https://stateofchildhoodobesity.org

p. 22–23 Omega 6: Omega 3 ratio in seed oil causing insulin resistance- Patterson E, Wall R, Fitzgerald GF, Ross RP, Stanton C. Health implications of high dietary omega-6 polyunsaturated Fatty acids. J Nutr Metab. 2012;2012:539426. doi: 10.1155/2012/539426. Epub 2012 Apr 5. PMID: 22570770; PMCID: PMC3335257.

p. 22 instability of PUFA - 6. Macari S. Why You Should Try The PUFA-Free Diet. Harper's BAZAAR. https://www.harpersbazaar.com/beauty/diet-fitness/a10965/pufa-free-diet/. Published May 21, 2015. Accessed July 4, 2022.

p. 23 linoleic acid content by oil chart - 5. Medical N. Oils Rich in Linoleic Acid. News - Medical.net. Published April 15, 2010. Accessed July 4, 2022. https://www.news- medical.net/health/Oils-Rich-in-Linoleic-Acid.aspx

p. 23 Dirty Dozen - 4. Environmental Working Group. EWG's 2022 Shopper's Guide to Pesticides in Produce TM. Summary. Accessed July 4, 2022. https://www.ewg.org/foodnews/summary.php

Chapter 5: Finding the Balanced Diet

p. 27 Animal proteins higher quality than plant protein: Lim MT, Pan BJ, Toh DWK, Sutanto CN, Kim JE. Animal Protein versus Plant Protein in Supporting Lean Mass and Muscle Strength: A Systematic Review and Meta-Analysis of Randomized Controlled Trials. Nutrients. 2021 Feb 18;13(2):661. doi: 10.3390/nu13020661. PMID: 33670701; PMCID: PMC7926405.

Chapter 7: The Family That Eats Together Bonds Together

p. 39 Children that have regular meal routines with their parents excel in almost all aspects of their life. Taken from the book: Carter, Christine. Raising Happiness: 10 Simple Steps for More Joyful Kids and Happier Parents. Ballantine Books, 2011.

p. 40 Starting family meals: 2. Starting family meals. Ellyn Satter Institute. Published February 24, 2019. Accessed July 4, 2022. https://www.ellynsatterinstitute.org/starting- family-meals/

Chapter 8: Expanding the Palate of Picky Eaters

p. 45 Picky eating can be an inheritable trait Cooke LJ, Haworth CM, Wardle J. Genetic and environmental influences on children's food neophobia. Am J Clin Nutr. 2007 Aug;86(2):428-33. doi: 10.1093/ajcn/86.2.428. PMID: 17684215.

p. 46 Tips on picky eaters: 3. Children's nutrition: 10 tips for picky eaters. Mayo Clinic. Published August 11, 2020. Accessed July 4, 2022. https://www.mayoclinic.org/healthy- lifestyle/childrens-health/in-depth/childrens-health/art-20044948

Chapter 10: Everything in Its Place

p. 51 Medical School Nutrition Training: Doctors need more nutrition education. News. Published May 9, 2017. Accessed July 4, 2022. https://www.hsph.harvard.edu/news/hsph- in-the-news/doctors-nutrition-education/

Chapter 11: Let's Get In the Kitchen

p. 56 Menu planning tips: The National Network for Childcare

Mother,

We want to thank you for instilling in us during childhood, the importance of healthy eating and fitness. Your guidance built our strong foundations and developed our understanding of what it means to care for our bodies. The dedication you've shown to our family's health has been an inspiration, and we are grateful for the habits (big and small) you have passed down to us. Your effortless passion makes all the difference in our lives.

We proudly support you on your journey to inspire others.

With love and appreciation,
Your boys - Jordan and Jonah

About the Author

Ruth J. Katz is a certified health coach from the Institute for Integrative Nutrition, an ICF-accredited Program.

Ruth has shared her knowledge, and expertise through various media and TV show outlets. in this book, she outlines an easier way to make healthy food fun for your kids. She nurtured her two sons into strong men by prioritizing preparing nutrient dense foods.

Ruth has been featured on national news shows including: The Today Show, Wall Street Journal, and CNN.

Luciana Pampalone Photography

Media links:

Ruth media reels

https://www.youtube.com/watch?v=Rv96f1SSeco

https://www.youtube.com/watch?v=V0122NeRNls "Coping with Food Allergies" posted by Wall Street Journal

http://ruthjkatz.com/

Printed in the USA
CPSIA information can be obtained
at www.ICGtesting.com
LVHW051508031123
762896LV00013B/1037